Cultural Awareness Teaching Techniques

Resource Handbook Number 4

by Jan Gaston

with an introduction by Raymond C. Clark

PRO LINGUA ⦵ ASSOCIATES

Published by Pro Lingua Associates
15 Elm Street
Brattleboro, Vermont 05301

SAN 216-0579

802-257-7779

Library of Congress Cataloguing in Publication Data

Gaston, Jan, 1946-
    Cultural awareness teaching techniques.

    (Resource handbook ; no. 4)
    1. Intercultural education. I. Title.
II. Series.
LC1099.G38   1984   370.19'6   84-18007

ISBN 0-86647-010-7

This book was set by Lisa Forrett Cook with display type by Stevens Photo-Typo-Graphics. It was printed and bound by The Book Press in Brattleboro, Vermont.
It was designed by Arthur A Burrows.

Printed in the United States of America.

Preface

The Blind Men and the Elephant

A Hindoo Fable

It was six men of Indostan
  To learning much inclined,
Who went to see the Elephant
  (Though all of them were blind),
That each by observation
  Might satisfy his mind.

The **First** approached the Elephant,
  And happening to fall
Against his broad and sturdy side,
  At once began to bawl:
"God bless me! but the Elephant
  Is very like a wall!"

The **Second** feeling of the tusk,
  Cried, "Ho! what have we here
So very round and smooth and sharp?
  To me 'tis mighty clear
This wonder of an Elephant
  Is very like a spear!"

The **Third** approached the animal,
  And happening to take
The squirming trunk within his hands,
  Thus boldly up and spake:
"I see," quoth he, "the Elephant
  Is very like a snake!"

The **Fourth** reached out an eager hand,
  And felt about the knee,
"What most this wondrous beast is like
  Is mighty plain," quoth he;
" 'Tis clear enough the Elephant
  Is very like a tree!"

The **Fifth** who chanced to touch the ear,
　Said: "E'en the blindest man
Can tell what this resembles most;
　Deny the fact who can,
This marvel of an Elephant
　Is very like a fan!"

The **Sixth** no sooner had begun
　About the beast to grope,
Than, seizing on the swinging tail
　That fell within his scope,
"I see," quoth he, "the Elephant
　Is very like a rope!"

And so these men of Indostan
　Disputed loud and long,
Each in his own opinion
　Exceeding stiff and strong,
Though each was partly in the right,
　And all were in the wrong!

The Moral:

So oft in theologic wars,
　The disputants, I ween,
Rail on in utter ignorance
　Of what each other mean,
And prate about an Elephant
　Not one of them has seen!

John Godfrey Saxe

Table of Contents

Acknowledgements

Sincere thanks to the students and my colleagues at the School for International Training who have helped give form to these ideas and activities. Technique 11, "Artifacts," is my version of an idea I borrowed from Wendyl Wason. Some of my ideas were first expressed in my own article "Cultural Orientation in the English as a Second Language Classroom." I have also quoted from Don Batchelder's article "The Green Banana," and I have adapted a section of Ted Gochenour's description of "The Owl." All these articles are taken from Beyond Experience, edited by Donald Batchelder and Susan Warner and published by The Experiment in International Living's Experiment Press.

Introduction

Cultural Awareness Teaching Techniques

> It is through the knowledge of languages and cultures that we best begin to know and comprehend the scope and significance of human experience in history, from ancient times to modern; it is through the knowledge of languages and cultures that we best learn to tolerate and appreciate cultural and linguistic diversity at home, to understand our contemporaries abroad and so achieve our full potential as citizens of the world.*

Cultural Awareness and Communication

We live in a time when the need for understanding and mutual respect across cultural boundaries is imperative. Implicit in the achievement of understanding and respect is the successful interchange between two human beings that we call communication. Language is, of course, a key component of communication, and although the accurate use of linguistic forms is necessary for effective communication, in most communicative situations, the communicators do more than simply talk to each other in grammatically well-constructed sentences; there has to be familiarity with the culture of the language being used by the communicators.

---

* From **"Language Competence and Cultural Awareness in the United States:** A Statement of the Position of the Joint National Committee for Languages and the Council for Language and other International Studies."

Introduction

Even between two fluent speakers of the same language there has to be some awareness of cultural differences. I still remember the parting words from a Nigerian student of mine who assured me "I will remember you until tomorrow." I understood his sentiment because I was aware that the English word "tomorrow" in a Nigerian context was a much less definite time expression than the day that follows today--or at least I hope so. The point is that language and culture, as we all know, are linked together and that communication, even between two people speaking the same language can be difficult if there is a cultural difference between the two speakers.

For the average person, a complete assimilation of a second culture may be even more impossible than speaking with flawless grammar and accurate pronunciation. What may be more realistic and valuable than striving for total assimilation of the target culture is the development of an awareness of culture and the intercultural skills that one develops on the way to cultural awareness.

Cultural Awareness and Intercultural Adjustment Skills

The goal of the teaching techniques collected in this book is cultural awareness, and although the term cultural awareness is not a new one in the field of language teaching, it may be useful to begin with a brief definition of the concept of cultural awareness as it is used in this book. Cultural awareness can be seen as the recognition that culture affects perception and that culture influences values, attitudes and behavior. The development of this awareness can be described as having four sequential stages leading ideally toward toleration and appreciation of cultural diversity.

Intercultural adjustment skills are a range of skills that are implicit in the concept of cultural awareness. These skills must be developed if we are to adjust to living in a new culture or even travel comfortably through a new culture. The concern of the language teacher becomes, then, the development of skills as well as awareness.

2

Introduction

In fact, one could make the case that the skills must be developed before an awareness will develop. Using the four stages of cultural awareness as a basis, we can describe four general skills that must be developed at each stage in the process.

STAGE ONE, RECOGNITION. At this stage we recognize the existence and pervasive influence of culture. For most of us, this begins with the growing consciousness of our own cultural group, and except for those individuals in extremely isolated cultural groups, we also begin to recognize the existence of other cultures. A pronouncement such as "I am an American" is the starting point, and implicit in this statement is the recognition that Americans do things in a particular way. Simultaneously, the concept of foreigner also begins to have meaning, and at this stage there is the recognition that foreigners do things differently. As we develop, so does our recognition that cultural differences are not only obvious and concrete (food, shelter, clothing), but subtle and abstract (values, attitudes, mores) as well. It is probably safe to say that as our recognition of foreign cultures increases, so too does our conscious recognition of our own cultural heritage.

At the recognition stage, the key skill is **non-judgemental observation.** This is the ability to see and describe culture with minimal judgement that what is seen is good or bad or right or wrong. In other words, we should avoid quick and easy labelling of cultural behavior as "funny" or "dumb" or "backward" or "progressive." Ideally, the inter-cultural traveller takes on the attitude of a scientist who simply reports what he sees. The first step toward understanding is seeing clearly.

Introduction

STAGE TWO, ACCEPTANCE/REJECTION. Almost simultaneously with our recognition of culture and cultural differences there is a reaction that is most often either positive or negative. Again the techniques in this book attempt to encourage a neutral, non-judgemental attitude of acceptance, but in fact what often occurs is rebellion against our own culture or rejection of the foreign culture.

The set of skills we hope to develop during this acceptance/rejection stage can be labelled **coping with ambiguity.** When we become aware of the fact that there is more than one way to behave or more than one way to organize society, it becomes necessary to live with a certain amount of ambiguity until we see enough of the total picture to see how the various pieces of the cultural puzzle fit together.

STAGE THREE, INTEGRATION/ETHNOCENTRISM. At this stage we reach either a somewhat more sophisticated point of view where we begin to act and think biculturally or, at the other extreme, we solidify our monocultual point of view into rigid ethnocentrism. For the ethnocentric individual, the road toward cultural awareness has come to an end.

At this third stage, where we have started to come to terms with the culture in an intercultural situation, we are beginning to develop into a bi-cultural being who is not only becoming more fluent in the language but is also beginning to take on a second identity. To achieve biculturalism, we must develop a set of skills that can be called the **ability to empathize.** This involves not only projecting ourselves into the role of a person in the target culture, but it also requires a willingness to let go of our close identity with our native culture. In the face of an impending identity crisis, when questions such as "Who am I, after all?" begin to emerge, our self image as "a 100% American," for example, must be sacrificed in order to embrace a new identity.

Introduction

STAGE FOUR, TRANSCENDENCE. When we reach the final stage of cultural awareness, we are able to value and appreciate our own cultural roots, whether they are native or acquired, and also to value and appreciate all other cultures as well. At this level of understanding, however, we are also able to transcend particular cultures and see their individual weaknesses and strengths, to become, in effect, a citizen of the world, searching for universals but also valuing the vitality and variety of earth's cultures.

Finally, after we have reached the point where we can transcend culture and see ourselves as a product of culture, but no longer a prisoner of culture, and when we can see the strengths and weaknesses of the cultures we embrace, we need a set of skills that can be labelled the **ability to respect.** This is what understanding is all about. It is important to note, however, that the ability to respect still allows for disagreement and criticism. We can, after all, adopt an attitude of "live and let live" while both showing respect for another way of doing things and questioning whether it is the only or best way.

The four stages outlined above are, of course, an idealized version of a process that in fact is not neatly separable into distinct phases like the metamorphosis of caterpillar to butterfly. For example, a strong case may be made for saying that stages one and two are really two aspects of an initial stage that could be called recognition and reaction. But because one of the objectives of this collection of techniques is to encourage people to withhold judgement, recognition and reaction have been separated. The point, however, is that these four stages are postulated to allow the teacher and students to focus attention on specific skills and attitudes that collectively lead toward cultural awareness in an orderly way.

More importantly, however, we should remind ourselves on a daily basis that theories and frameworks such as the four stages of cultural awareness apply only to an idealized student, and that the students in our classrooms are individuals who not only look different from each other, but also think, feel and grow in ways that never quite match the idealized "we" of the preceding paragraphs. Ultimately, the journey toward cultural awareness is made by individuals who, like the six blind men in Saxe's poem in the preface, may never know the whole truth or the best answer, but whose handicap should not prevent them from the search.

Applicability of the Techniques

The techniques presented in this book were developed in an intensive English program conducted in the U.S. Furthermore, the composition of the classes in which these techniques were developed was of students from a variety of linguistic/cultural backgrounds. This kind of class lends itself most easily to the goal of developing cultural awareness because there is a variety of cultures represented in the class. However, throughout this book the author has suggested ways in which the techniques can be used effectively with monocultural classes.

In general, the techniques will be most effective with students who have an intermediate/advanced command of the target language because discussion/ conversation is a key activity in most of the 20 techniques. Secondly, when the entire collection of techniques is used as a sequenced program, the program should be used in the context of a teaching / learning situation where the target language is spoken in the immediate environment. Techniques 16-18, for example, do require extramural excursions as one part of the techniques.

To present the techniques in this book in the clearest and most specific way, they are described as techniques for an English as a second language classroom in the U.S. But with modification, the techniques can easily be used in a variety of situations, from teaching French in France, for example, or even with additional modification, teaching any foreign language in an environment where the language is not widely spoken outside the classroom. For that matter, these techniques can also be adapted for use in a social studies class or in a course on cultural awareness where there is no second language component. And although the techniques can be used with very little modification by teachers of English as a second language in the U.S. with a multicultural class, the description of the technique should be viewed as a suggested way to do things, and not as the only way or even the best way, for as we all know, no two classes are ever alike.

As desirable as cultural awareness may be, from the teacher's point of view, it must be remembered, that most students come to the language classroom with a more mundane motive-- to learn a language. The teaching of cultural awareness needs to be approached, therefore, with a certain amount of caution. If the students are not ready for classroom work that seems to be irrelevant or superfluous to the goal of learning a language, an indirect approach may work better; most students will readily accept the techniques in this book as a form of conversation practice. And of course, these techniques for the teaching of cultural aware- ness will, in fact, promote language learning, especially because the activities are carried out in the context of a language classroom and under the guidance of a language teacher.

Introduction

Sequence and Format of the Techniques

The twenty techniques in this book are arranged in a sequence that generally follows the four stages of cultural awareness. The overall goal of the first five techniques is to begin the process of cultural awareness by introducing students to the concept that culture pervades our lives and that cultures are organized in different ways. The students are asked to examine their own cultures and make comparisons with the target culture and, if applicable, with the cultures of other students in the class. During this phase, the skill of non-judgemental observation is introduced and practiced.

The second group of five techniques focuses on reactions to cultural differences and gives the students the opportunity to practice the skill of coping with ambiguity in a constructive way.

In the third group of five techniques, the students are encouraged to accept selected aspects of the target culture by participating in the culture as fully as they can while simultaneously surrendering some of their own culturally-bound ways of behaving.

The final five give the students the opportunity not only to learn more about the target culture, but also to build an attitude of intelligent and liberated respect for cultures, both their own and others. The last two techniques in particular are designed to leave the students with a general set of skills and attitudes that will carry over into future intercultural experiences, whether in the target culture or in cultures yet to be encountered in the student's future.

The format for presenting the techniques in this book is a reflection of a basic premise of experiential education. First, the students are introduced to a structured experience--one that may take place either within the four walls of the classroom or outside in the real world. Then with the assignment and guidelines firmly in hand, they are asked to do something, and finally, with the teacher's guidance they are asked to reflect upon what they have done and arrive at conclusions. The numbered procedural steps, the heart of each technique, reflect these three stages. The last numbered step in the procedure is labelled "synthesis" to emphasize the importance of the final step. The synthesis is also closely related to the objectives which are stated at the beginning of each technique. Although the objectives are not stated as classic behavioral objectives, they and the concluding synthesis are based on the concept that learning can be facilitated if there is a clear statement of what is to be learned and a conclusion that in some way shows that in fact something has (or has not) been learned.

The sequenced procedural steps are accompanied by explanatory notes from the author. She uses her own experience with these techniques to give the reader further detail on how to conduct the techniques, and she offers suggestions on how to adapt them to specific teaching situations. Implicit in her suggestions is the notion that the user of these techniques must, in fact, use them only as general guidelines and must constantly make her own adaptations to fit the unique aspects of her own teaching situation.

Suggestions
for the Teacher

General Teaching Suggestions

A few additional suggestions of a general nature should be kept in mind to help insure the success of these techniques in the classroom.

First, establish and maintain a comfortable, non-threatening atmosphere in which the students will be willing to take risks and express themselves. As the teacher you can foster a comfortable classroom environment by being a non-judgemental reflective listener. This implies accepting student responses and taking them seriously, even though you may not personally agree with what a student is saying. You can encourage the students to take risks by occasionally taking risks yourself, and you can guard against unnecessary tension by injecting humor from time to time.

A second suggestion is to be as clear as possible about the objective of each technique so that the students know the "why" of what they are doing. At the conclusion of each technique, you should also find an opportunity to refer to the objective, and together with the students make an assessment of whether you have achieved the objective.

Finally, keep in mind that your students are individuals and they not only respond differently to what you are doing, but they progress at different rates, not only as language learners, but also as human beings adjusting to and assimilating a new culture.

Suggestions For The Teacher

Suggestions for Leading a Discussion

Because discussion is an activity that is central to the success of all the techniques in this collection, the following suggestions for leading discussions may prove helpful.

The purpose and ground rules of discussion will vary from culture to culture, making it important at the beginning of any series of cultural awareness techniques to talk about discussions. Some leading questions for doing this are:

> What is a discussion?
>
> What is the goal of a discussion?
>
> How is a discussion conducted?
>
> How do you feel about discussion?

If the students represent a variety of cultural backgrounds, this discussion of discussions should at least lead toward some recognition that a group of people talking together about a common topic can operate in different ways. Because you are asking the class to take part in discussion, your own view of the purpose and procedure of discussion should also be presented, although tactically it may be best for you to save your views on discussion until the students have expressed their views.

After the initial clarification of the purpose of discussions, the next step is to establish some ground rules for the class. Because discussion is by nature participatory and democratic, it follows that the ground rules themselves should be established as democratically as possible. In most cases, the class's ground rules will result in agreements and rules such as these:

> The discussion should (or should not) have a leader.
>
> The leader will be chosen in this way:

Suggestions For The Teacher

The role of the teacher will be:

How, when, and where will mistakes in the language be corrected, if at all.

Only one person speaks at a time.

Everyone is expected to participate; this includes speaking as well as listening.

Participants are free to ask each other questions.

Participants are free to give their ideas and opinions, and these are respected by everyone in the group.

Disagreement is not a rejection of another person.

It is helpful to post these rules in the classroom for later reference and possible revision.

Once the ground rules are established and posted, two additional ground rules for the teacher should be kept in mind. First, before each discussion begins it is imperative that the class understands what is being discussed and why it is being discussed. Writing the topic in large letters on the board is one way of helping to focus the discussion. One of the great problems with discussion, as we all know, is straying from the topic.

A second useful ongoing procedure is to review the discussion process itself periodically. It can be initiated by reference to the ground rules to see if they are being followed or not and to see if there are changes to be made. This periodic evaluation is also useful for bringing out problems in the dynamics of participant interchange. Sometimes, for example, someone is being excluded, or there may be a participant who is dominating or intimidating others. Or someone may not be participating. Whatever the problem, it may not come to the surface unless there is a structured opportunity for it to do so.

Suggestions For The Teacher

Finally, here are a few tips for facilitating discussions.

Give the students a few moments to think about and organize their answers and responses. Sometimes hesitation to speak indicates only that the student is groping for words and ways to express his thoughts.

Be very quick to spot dominators and, if necessary, take them aside to talk about their domination. Sometimes, of course, dominators are simply the most fluent members of the class.

Lack of participation does not necessarily mean a student has no opinion or he is not interested in the discussion. Some students appreciate being called on.

Being a non-participating observer is an excellent opportunity to listen not to what the students are saying, but how they are saying it. For that reason, it is helpful from time to time to have someone else lead the class while you detach yourself from the discussion and take notes on your students' linguistic problems.

Although discussion is a critical part of these techniques, sometimes a discussion format just doesn't work very well with a particular class. In that event it is a mistake to insist on discussion, but you don't have to give up on doing cultural awareness sessions. The discussion can simply be replaced by a teacher-led question and answer session, instead of a discussion.

If the class is multicultural, there may be, despite the class ground rules, some deep-seated cultural bases for problems in classroom dynamics. These problems won't easily and quickly go away; they have to be accepted with understanding and patience. Although the process of cultural awareness leads toward transcendence of and liberation from culturally-based behavior, the process takes time.

1.

Family Tree

The students draw diagrams of the structures of their families. They question each other about their families, leading to an awareness of how their cultures shape the concept of "family."

Objective

To show that the concept and structure of "family" is influenced by one's culture.

Procedure

1. The students draw their family trees.

This step can be done in class or assigned as homework.

This technique runs more smoothly if the students know the vocabulary for family relationships. Therefore I usually go over the vocabulary at some point during this step.

To help the students get started, I sometimes draw a sample family tree on the blackboard. However, I encourage them to be creative and to design their own trees. I usually participate in this exercise along with the students.

Family Tree

If all the students are from one culture, this exercise can still be effective. For example, in a class of Brazilians, one person had Japanese parents while another's parents were German, and that turned out to be an interesting way for these students to learn about the diversity in their own country. Even if students from the same country come from similar family backgrounds, this exercise still allows them to become aware of their perceptions of "family."

2. Post the drawings for the students to study.

3. The students ask each other questions about their families.

   It is important to keep the students on the topic of their families.

4. Lead a discussion on the subject of families. Focus questions:

   a. When you use the word "family," whom do you include?

   b. Where were your parents, grandparents and great-grandparents born?

   This question can reveal diversities and similarities among different cultures, or within one culture.

   c. Do you think the size of your family is common in your country? Are there places in your country where families are smaller or larger?

   d. Is the way your family lives and relates similar to most other families in your country? In what ways is it similar or different?

   Before students answer this question, I usually give them a few minutes to think. First, they have to think about how their own families live and then about how that relates to other families.

Family Tree

In the discussion, I especially watch for an assumption that <u>every</u> family in a particular country relates in the same way. Sometimes this assumption can stifle others from the same country who have a different background.

Synthesis

5. **Each student makes concluding statements based on the objectives of the exercise.**

   I find it helpful to use a clear focus question. Some possibilities are:

a. What did you learn about your view of your family?

b. Why are there differences in the way families are structured?

2.

Home

**The students draw floor plans for their homes and
discuss the similarities and differences.**

Objective

To discover and compare the different ways people
organize and use one of man's basic needs: Shelter.

Procedure

1. **Each student is given a large piece of paper and
   asked to draw a floor plan of his house, including
   some of the major pieces of furniture.**

   At first glance this exercise may seem simplistic
   but it gives the students the opportunity to
   talk about something familiar and personal
   while beginning to see that culture has a definite
   role in how we define and create "home."

   I would suggest that you do your own floor
   plan and present yours first as a model for others
   to follow. A lot of detail on furniture is not
   necessary.

   If your class is composed of immigrants, you
   might ask them to draw two floor plans--one of
   their home as it was in the native country and
   one of their home in this country. In this case,
   in Step 3 you might want to ask students to
   compare the similarities and differences in their
   two homes.

Home

If your class is all one nationality, Step 2 may serve the purpose of sharing personal information and Step 3 could include similarities and differences between their drawings and yours.

2. **Each student is given a limited amount of time to show and describe his house.**

   With a small group, give everyone a limited amount of time to describe his home, and with a large group, ask the students to form groups of 4-5. In either case, it will help the students in their own descriptions and attempts to find commonalities and differences with others if you explain your drawing first. Try to help the students get beneath a superficial description by asking them to include information about what happens in each room:

   Which rooms seem to be central?

   Which rooms serve more than one function?

   How does the house reflect the need for privacy?

   Who uses the different rooms?

3. **Ask the students to identify similarities and differences among their drawings.**

   It might be helpful to put some of the responses on the board to focus the discussion in this step and in Step 4.

Synthesis

4. **Ask each student to look for something unique in his own floor plan and something that seems unique in some of his classmates' plans. Secondly, have them speculate on the reasons for the unique features they identified.**

   I like to allow the students a few minutes silently planning their summaries before I ask them to make synthesizing statements.

3.

Observation and Interpretation

The students list a number of observations about
the target culture. They examine their observations
to see which ones could be interpretations.

Objective

> To establish the difference between observation
> and interpretation.
>
> To realize that oversimplifications (e.g., "All
> Americans are rich.") are unfair and limiting.

Procedure

1. The students make a list of observations they
   have made about living and studying in the target
   culture.

Observation and Interpretation

In order to help the students get started, I give them some examples of areas about which they can make observations, e.g., food, relationships, dress, nonverbal communication.

2. **Select a few statements from each student and write them down so that everyone can easily see them.**

Because we will use the board in the next step, I write these observations on a flip chart. Rolls of brown wrapping paper are also useful for this kind of work.

3. **Establish definitions for observation and interpretation.**

I write the words "observation" and "interpretation" on the board and ask the students to give a definition and examples of both. Or, I write up an example of an observation and an interpretation on the board and ask the group to describe the difference between the two statements. An example might be: "American food is terrible" (interpretation) and "Americans do not generally use hot spices in their food" (observation). Another example might be: "People here are unfriendly" (interpretation) and "People here generally say 'Hi' and continue walking" (observation).

4. **Ask the students to identify which of their statements in Step 2 are observations and which are interpretations. Then have the students change the interpretations to observations.**

It is important in this step that the students realize the difference between observations and interpretations. Sometimes it is difficult to differentiate, and the students may find this in some of their examples. If there is disagreement as to whether a statement is one or the other, simply ask the student who believes it is an interpretation to change it to an observation. The act of changing these statements clearly demonstrates the focus of this exercise.

Synthesis

5. **Conclude with a discussion of the following questions:**

   a. **Why is it important to know and practice the difference between observation and interpretation?**

   b. **How can you improve your own skills in observing?**

   The experience of changing statements in Step 4 is often powerful because the difference between the two becomes clear, and the participants begin to see the implications of interpreting and observing. The questions in this step give the students the opportunity to deepen their understanding of the difference and to make some generalizations about what they have learned.

4.

Cultural Statements

Each student brings to class something from his culture that is personally meaningful.

Objectives

To share a personally meaningful aspect of one's own culture.

To begin defining the characteristic of one's own culture.

To promote appreciation and respect for the individuals in the class and their backgrounds.

Cultural Statements

Procedure

1. Each student brings something to class which is both personally meaningful and representative of some aspect of his culture.

I give the students a day or two to think about the assignment and choose something that is personally meaningful. They may not be able to find an object, but they could bring a picture.

It would be helpful to give some personal examples. They might be:

Pictures of your hometown.

A book of your favorite poems.

An article of clothing.

A picture of a national monument.

A handcrafted object.

The purpose of this step is for the students to think about their own cultures and begin defining what it means to be from a particular culture.

If the students in the class are from the same culture, the directions for this step would be the same, but you might want to ask the students not to talk about the assignment with each other outside of class.

2. One by one the students show what they have brought and speak about it.

Set a time limit for each presentation.

This is not really a time for students to ask each other questions about each other's cultures. It is a time to listen to others sharing something personal. Therefore, I don't allow the listeners to ask questions.

Cultural Statements

Synthesis

3. After everyone has made their presentations, ask them to discuss what they have seen and heard.

Give the students a minute or two to think about what they have seen and heard. To guide the discussion, these questions might be helpful:

a. What is one thing (either personal or cultural) that you have learned from each person in the class?

b. What did you learn about your own culture in doing this exercise?

5.

Short Readings

A short reading serves as the basis for a written and oral exploration of cultural differences and cultural adjustment.

Objective

To compare a single aspect of one's own and the target culture.

To begin looking at the cultural adjustment process.

Procedure

1. **Give the students a short article on some aspect of U.S. culture to read.**

   For the purposes of this exercise, I prefer articles that go beyond the level of information and get at attitudes and values. A list of topics and a specific example are given after the synthesis of this technique.

2. **Ask the students to write an article on the same topic about their own culture.**

The initial article given to the students can serve as a model for their own articles. You may want to give the students a definite limit or length. Encourage them to think first; then write.

If your students are all from the same culture, ask them to write on the same topic without discussing the topic with others in the class. Different points of view will still emerge from the assignment.

3. **Reproduce all the articles and give the students an opportunity to read them.**

Before reproducing the articles, consider these three options in regard to correction:

a. Reproduce the articles as they were turned in, with no changes.

b. Change only the problems that might cause confusion or misunderstanding.

c. Correct everything (If you choose this option, you may want to offer the students the opportunity to rewrite their articles).

4. **Ask the students to write two or three questions they would like to ask about one of the other articles.**

Writing out the questions often helps the students get beyond superficial reading. If your group is from the same culture, ask them to write a list of the similarities and differences found among the articles.

5. **The students ask each other their questions.**

For a monocultural group, ask them to compare their culture with U.S. culture. This can lead into a discussion of adjustment problems, as suggested in the next step.

Synthesis

6. **Ask the students to discuss these two questions:**

   a. **Considering only the topic of our articles, if you were going to visit each other's cultures, what would be similar and what would be different?**

   b. **What would you have to adjust to?**

   c. **Do you think that adjustment would be easy or difficult for you?**

SUGGESTED TOPICS

Clothing	Crime	Life Style
Eating Habits	Health	Patriotism
Fads	Heroes	Sex
Family	Holidays	Sports Events
Food	Humor	

SAMPLE ARTICLE

SMALLTOWN DAILY, March

Students Prepare for Spring Vacation

By BILL LOHMANN

***DAYTONA BEACH, Florida (UPI) — It's time for the annual spring pilgrimage to Florida. Thousands of college students are packing their bags, leaving the cold north and traveling south.

About one million students will spend part of March or April in Florida, forgetting their books, problems and sometimes their manners. They eat like bears, drink like fish, and search for sun, fun and sex.

Thousands will go to Fort Lauderdale, but most (about 300,000) will go to Daytona Beach. In spite of inflation and recession, more students are expected this year than last year. "Students aren't affected by the economy," said an author of a guide book to Florida.

In order to save money, six or seven students will stay in one hotel room, or stay in a tent at a campground. And many students sleep on the beach during the day and wander the streets at night.

Though most of the students aren't rich, local merchants welcome them. If each students spent only $100 during his stay on Daytona Beach, that would add $30 million into the area's economy. "The community is very glad they're here," said one businessman.

But the student invasion makes life difficult for the police. "The majority of them are decent kids just down here to have a good time," said one policeman. "But it takes only one jerk and we've got a problem."

One woman who has worked for thirty-two years as a bartender believes that every spring is basically the same, though the students change. "If you've seen one spring break, you've seen them all," she said. "It's insane all the time."

Taken from Smalltown Daily, John Miller and Raymond C. Clark, Pro Lingua Associates, Brattleboro, VT, 1984.

6. Nonverbal Interviews

In pairs, the students interview each other nonverbally. Information learned about each other as well as the experience of the exercise, is shared in the group.

Objectives

To learn about others in the class and their countries.

To become aware that communication in new situations, particularly when a new language is involved, can be frustrating and ambiguous. It often requires creating some new ways of conveying meaning.

Procedure

1. **The students pair up and interview each other nonverbally.**

    Large pieces of paper should be posted around the room and magic markers made available. Explain that everyone will have a partner, and these two people will find out as much as they can about each other (including information about each other's countries).

Nonverbal Interviews

But these interviews must happen nonverbally. Each pair will use one of the large pieces of paper and draw pictures, but they cannot write words or numbers. When this part of the exercise is finished, the students will briefly tell the rest of the class what they learned about their partners.

I give the students 20-25 minutes. This may seem like a long time, but it forces the students to find out more about each other and to devise new and more creative ways of conveying meaning and information. I also tell the students when half the time has passed and remind them that the object of the exercise is to find out information about <u>each other</u>. Sometimes, one of the partners will dominate. When the time is up, give the students a few minutes to walk around and look at the other papers.

2. **The students give information about their partners to the rest of the group.**

   The students are learning more about each other and checking to see if they gave and received clear messages. It is not uncommon in this step that some of the information may be inaccurate. If this happens, be sure to allow the students to give the correct information about themselves and their countries.

3. **Lead a discussion based on the following questions:**

   a. **How did you feel during this exercise?**

   Some typical responses are: tired, confused, excited, anxious, silly.

   b. **Was it easy or difficult for you to communicate without words? Why?**

   c. **What problems did you have in trying to communicate?**

Some typical responses to this question are: "different interpretations," "no clear way to express a particular message," "one misunderstanding affected the communication that followed."

4. **Write some of the responses to questions a. and c. on the board to guide the discussion in the next step.**

Synthesis

5. **Ask the students to reflect and comment on the purpose of this exercise.**

I find it helpful to begin this discussion by asking the students to recall their first week in the U.S., beginning with their arrival at the airport. After giving them a minute to think, refer to the responses on the board. In a group discussion, ask if they had any of the same feelings (question a.) and any of the same problems (question c.). Encourage the students to give brief examples from their own experiences.

Conclude by stating the second objective of this technique and then give an example or two from the students' experiences to help make the objective clear.

7.

Picture Drawing

The students are shown a picture and asked to reproduce it from memory. The various reproductions are examined and discussed, leading toward the conclusion that we perceive the world differently, according to our personal and cultural backgrounds.

Objective

To show that a common experience often results in different perceptions, and that what we perceive is shaped by our previous experience.

Procedure

1. **The teacher shows a picture to the class, allowing them to look at it for one minute.**

    I try to use a picture, photograph or slide of a countryside scene, one that is not familiar to the students and not too complex. If the picture is too busy, the students' discussion might focus more on the objects than on the similarities and differences they find in each others' drawings.

Picture Drawing

If the group is large, I ask the students to break into smaller groups (even numbers if possible), each group with its own picture.

2. **The teacher removes the picture from view and the students each draw from memory.**

    As an additional option, depending on the students' language ability, I ask them to write a paragraph describing what they saw.

    In giving the instructions to draw a picture, I reassure the students that this exercise is not a drawing contest. The purpose is not to choose the prettiest or most accurate original.

3. **The students find a partner and compare their drawings.**

    There is often some initial nervousness and laughter as the students show each other their drawings.

4. **The teacher asks the pairs of students to identify the similarities and differences they found in their drawings.**

5. **After the paired discussions, each student is asked to identify what he was particularly attracted to in the picture.**

    After this step, I have everybody look at all the drawings.

6. **The teacher leads the class in a discussion of the exercise.**

    Some leading questions are:

    a. What did you find when you compared your drawing to someone else's?

    b. Why do you think you drew things that were different from your partner's?

c. What attracted you in the picture? Do you know why? What effect did this have on your perception of the total picture?

7. The class is shown the original drawing again and asked to compare it silently with their own drawings.

It is important for the students to have the opportunity to compare their drawings with the original, but I try to help them avoid judgements about how "right" or "wrong" their drawings are. I encourage them to see what they emphasized in their own drawings.

Synthesis

8. The class reflects on the objective of the exercise.

This step can be done in a variety of ways. Generally, I ask the students two questions and give them a few minutes to think about and write their responses. The questions:

a. What was the purpose of this exercise?

b. What did you learn?

By asking the class to think through and write out their answers, the final discussion is often more to the point.

8.

Country Talks

Individually or as a team, the students give talks about their countries. After all the countries have been presented, a summary discussion focuses on cultural relativity.

Objectives

To increase knowledge and awareness of the specific cultures in the classroom.

To introduce the concept of cultural relativity (each culture has its own particular view of what is "real").

Procedure

1. Using the classroom walls, put up a large piece of paper for each country represented in the class. The name of a country is written at the top of the paper.

   This exercise requires at least two countries to be represented in the class.

2. Ask the students to move around the room and write questions they might have on each of the countries. The questions are written on the large pieces of paper, i.e., all questions for Saudi Arabia are written on the paper marked Saudi Arabia.

Country Talks

Explain this exercise to the students a day or two before it is done in class. Ask them to be thinking of questions they have for each country. I usually include a sheet for the U.S. so that the students have the opportunity to question me.

During this phase of the exercise, I help the students formulate their questions. I find the questions vary considerably. Some examples from groups I have worked with are:

a. "Do you have television in Brazil?"

b. "Why are Japanese people so quiet?"

c. "What is the structure of the government in Mexico?"

d. "How do the people in your country feel about nuclear weapons?"

3. **Once the questions are written, give the students an opportunity to read all of them. Then allow time for questions of clarification on what has been written.**

   If the class is small, it is possible to focus on each paper one at a time. Questions on grammar may also come up at this time.

4. **Each individual or team representing a country is given an assigned class period to respond to the questions with a country talk.**

   Depending on the language ability of the group, class sessions usually range from 30-60 minutes. There is no single best pattern for scheduling these sessions--one a day or one or two a week. If they are spaced too far apart, the students might lose a sense of continuity and purpose.

   Encourage the students to use visuals in their presentation.

   If there is more than one person representing a country, suggest that they meet as a group to plan their session. This is often not an easy task because the students soon find that even though they are from the same country, their perspectives on their country differ. You may want to meet with them briefly to help them solve their differences and work together.

For the actual presentation, ask the students not to write a speech and read it. Ask them to bring notes and speak spontaneously.

Generally, I note language problems and use this information in later language lessons. At times, students have asked me to write down errors as they were speaking and afterwards we met to discuss them. At other times I have given students the option of recording their talks on tape and then meeting afterwards to review the tape for language errors.

Synthesis

5. When all the presentations have been made, give the students time to write or just think about these questions; then follow up with a class discussion.

a. What did you learn about the other countries represented in the class?

b. Have you changed any of your opinions or impressions of the countries?

c. What did you learn about your country from the questions of others?

d. What was the purpose of this exercise?

9.

Stereotypes

The students engage in stereotyping each other and then talk through the cause and effect of stereotypes.

Objectives

To define "stereotypes" and identify where they originate.

To understand the effect stereotypes have on our perception of and relationships with others.

Procedure

1. Ask the class what a stereotype is.

It might be helpful to the students if their responses are written up on the board where everyone can see them. It is important that the students understand the meaning of stereotype before going on.

Another variation that I use is a picture that depicts a stereotype. After the students have studied it, I ask them about it: "What do you see in the picture?" "What does the picture say?"

2. Ask the students what stereotypes they have of Americans.

Students are often reluctant to begin, fearing they might offend you. So it might be helpful to give a couple of examples. Again, the responses should be written up where everyone can see them. At the conclusion of this technique there is a list of stereotypical statements I have sometimes used.

Another variation is to have the students draw only a picture which shows a stereotype of an American. These are posted for everyone to see.

3. Post a large sheet of paper for each country represented in the class. Ask the students to write or draw stereotypes for each others' countries.

At this point in the exercise, the students are usually beginning to _feel_ what it is like to be stereotyped, and they show their feelings through laughter and astonishment that others could think such things about their cultures. I have never had anyone get angry -- probably because everyone is a "victim."

If the students are all from the same country, ask them to identify stereotypes that exist within their own culture.

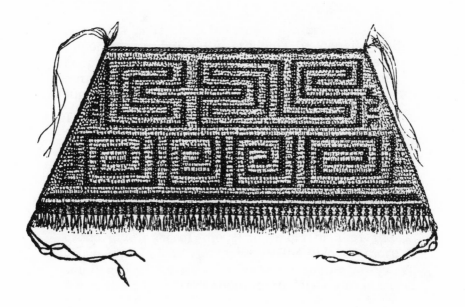

Synthesis

4. **Lead a discussion based on these questions:**

   a. **What do you think about what others wrote or drew about your country?**

   b. **How did you feel when you saw these comments about your country?**

   c. **Why do you think stereotypes exist?**

   d. **How are stereotypes destroyed?**

   Be sure to distinguish <u>think</u> in question a. and <u>feel</u> in question b.

   If all the students are from the same culture, change question a. to: "What do you think about this list?" and "Do you have any thoughts about what we have written? If so, what?" And change questions b. to: "How did you feel as we were making this list?"

STEREOTYPES

Americans are rich

    wear cowboy boots and eat hotdogs
    and hamburgers

    drive big cars

    shout a lot

    are very aggressive

    have superficial relationships

    do not care about old people

    do not care about family relationships

    lack discipline

    always think everything American is best

    are disrespectful of age and status

    talk a lot but say little

    think only about money

    do not know anything about the rest
    of the world

    worry more about their possessions
    than their children

    are friendly

10.

The First Days

Thinking back on the first week of living in the U.S., the students discuss the thoughts and feelings, circumstances and people that initially affected them. This is followed by a discussion of attitudes and actions that can help one be more comfortable and in control in new and unfamiliar cultural situations.

Objectives

To become aware that our initial interaction with a situation can affect our future relationship with it.

To identify actions and attitudes that help create comfort and relaxation and the ability to stay in control in new and unfamiliar cultural circumstances.

Procedure

1. **Ask the students to reflect on their first week in the U.S.**

   I ask the students to think about and write some brief notes on the following questions about their first week of living in the U.S.:

   a. What situation(s) or circumstance(s) do you especially remember?

   b. Were there any people who had a particular effect on you? Who were they? What affect did they have?

c. What feelings and thoughts did you have the first week you were in the U.S.?

d. Did you do anything that first week that helped you feel and act more comfortable and relaxed? What?

Another option for Step 1 is to give the students the questions a few days before this technique is done in class. This will give them more time to think about the questions.

2. The students discuss their responses to the four questions.

It is important that the students not take too much class time with lengthy tales of their experiences. Encourage those who give personal examples to be brief and to the point. As the one leading this discussion, I try to keep the objective of this exercise clearly in everybody's mind.

Synthesis

3. The students make concluding statements based on the objectives of this exercise.

I conclude this exercise by leading a discussion on the following two questions:

a. What effect has your initial experience in the U.S. had on the rest of the time you have been here?

b. Imagine that next week you are going to a country you have never been to before. You do not speak the language of that country very well. What could you do and what attitudes could you have that would help you in this situation?

11.

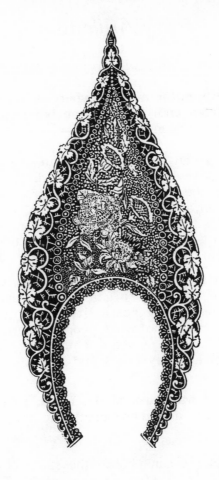

Artifacts

The students examine a collection of cultural artifacts and try to understand what they represent. The process of trying to understand another culture is examined.

Objectives

To practice the skill of observation.

To practice entering another culture by looking for the meaning behind cultural artifacts.

To examine how meaning is ascribed.

Artifacts

Procedure

1. **The students enter a room where a variety of artifacts from one culture have been put in various spots around the room.**

    This step can be likened to entering a museum where the exhibits are unlabeled. It is preferable for the artifacts to come from a culture that is unfamiliar to the students. It may be a culture that you have lived in or known, or one that a resource person (someone who is not part of the class) is familiar with.

    The artifacts should be objects that will allow the students to gain some insight into the culture. Some possibilities are: clothing, jewelry, toys, photos of people, tools, utensils, arts and crafts, symbols, emblems, photos of dwellings and key crops and foods.

2. **The students walk around the room, surveying all the objects and then select one they would like to study.**

    Two students can choose the same object as long as they study it separately. Two different interpretations can be a useful point of discussion.

3. **The students study their objects for five minutes. I encourage them to ask themselves such questions as:**

    a. **What kind of society does it come from?**

    b. **What meaning does it hold for the people of this culture?**

    c. **What is my reaction to this object?**

    d. **How would I describe it?**

    The purpose of this step is to give the students some guidance and also allow them to explore their objects in whatever way they choose.

    I sometimes put the study questions, such as those listed above, on the board.

Artifacts

It is important to tell the students they will have an opportunity to ask and receive answers to their specific questions at the end of the exercise.

4. **The class sits in a circle, each student with his object. Each student has one or two minutes to report to the others his experience with the object -- any thoughts, feelings and questions.**

    The length of time I give to the students will depend on their language proficiency.

    You may need to encourage some students with a few questions. These may be helpful:

    a. What were you thinking as you looked at your object?

    b. Did you have any particular feelings?

    c. What ideas did this object give you about the people who use/made it?

    d. Did it remind you of anything in your own culture?

    At this point, some students may want to ask specific questions. You may have to help them stay on the subject of their own experience.

5. **The teacher asks the group to put the pieces together to make a comprehensive picture of the culture. The two key questions are:**

    a. **Describe the culture these artifacts come from.**

    b. **How did you arrive at these conclusions?**

    Tackle the questions one at a time. I record the responses to the first question on the board or large sheets of paper so everyone can see them. It is not important if responses are dissimilar or contradictory.

    The second question may be difficult for students to understand. It might be helpful if you ask a specific question. For example, "Misako, you think that art is important to the people of this culture. Why do you think that is true?" or "Yousef, you said you think the people of this culture are poor. Why?"

The students may have differences of opinion, and there should be an opportunity to discuss the differences. It is important in this step to help the students see <u>how</u> they gave meaning to the objects and to the culture.

6. **The students have an opportunity to ask their specific questions regarding the objects and the culture.**

   The purpose of this step is for the students to receive answers to their questions -- it is not a time to see who was "right" and who was "wrong."

Synthesis

7. **Hold a brief discussion on this question: What did you learn from doing this exercise?**

   A good starting point for the discussion is to restate the objectives of the technique and ask the students if they were able to search for and ascribe meaning without becoming judgemental.

12.

Cultural Scene

The students observe a short skit and then try to understand what happened from a cultural point of view.

Objectives

To practice observation skills.

To investigate the way meaning is ascribed.

Procedure

1. Three or four students from the same culture enact a scene from their culture while others in the class observe.

Cultural Scene

If you do not have three or four students from the same culture in your class, or the students are all from one culture, invite some Americans to enact a scene. Family life would be a good topic. Sample scenes might be: Dinner table, a teenager asking for the car keys or getting back late from a date, visit from a neighbor.

A scene should be about five minutes, and for whoever performs, it is important to remember that the purpose is not to trick the observers or make the relationships and interactions too obvious. Rather, the purpose is to provide practice in observing and understanding the relationship between observing and interpreting.

An alternative to a cultural scene is a simulated culture. A scenario is given below.

2. **When the skit is over lead a discussion in which the following questions are asked of the observers:**

   a. What happened?

   b. What is your interpretation of what you saw?

   It is best to ask these two questions together because observation and interpretation are inter-related. It might help the discussion if you ask the observers to talk about the scene in chronological order. Alternatively, you might want to ask the questions and give the observers a few minutes to write responses.

   The written responses are not to be handed in; they are used as notes during the discussion.

   The performers are asked to listen. At this point they should not respond to what the observers say.

3. **The observers ask the performers questions about the skit.**

   Two kinds of questions are often asked: those that can be relatively easily answered -- "Was the father angry at the daughter in the scene?" and those that cannot -- "Why do you greet each other in that way?"

The second kind of question is often a "why" question that can often be answered only with "It's our culture; it's the way we do things." The questioner is often dissatisfied with this answer, so if you know something about the culture of the questioner, you might ask him a few "why" questions. This often shows that such questions are not easily answered.

Synthesis

4. **Discuss these two questions:**

   a. **Some of you saw things that others did not see. Some of you made different interpretations of the scene. Why?**

   b. **What is the effect of judging another culture as "strange," "wrong," or "funny?"**

A SCENARIO

General Briefing

This exercise involves two male-female couples. It is more effective if male students play the roles of males and likewise for the females. However, if your class does not include at least two males or females, it can be done by having males play the roles of females or vice versa.

There are two cultures involved. Couple A are from Country X and Couple B assume their own cultural identities. It may work a little better if Couple B are both from the same culture, e.g. both Brazilians, but if that is not possible the two students playing Couple B represent a culturally-mixed marriage, e.g. an Italian married to a Swiss.

The two couples are instructed separately. They are given the briefing sheets and asked to study them for a few minutes before beginning the role play.

*Adapted from "The Owl" by Theodore Gochenour in <u>Beyond Experience</u>, Donald Batchelder and Elizabeth G. Warner, eds., The Experiment Press, Brattleboro, VT., 1977, pp. 125-129.

Cultural Scene

Briefing Sheet #1 - Country X

You are a member of Country X, an ancient land which has been isolated from the rest of the world. X-ians have a way of life which has not changed for many years.

In Country X, women are the natural leaders, administrators, heads of households, principal artists, owners of wealth and rulers of the state. Men rarely work outside the home. They keep house, cook and care for the children. Education is very important for the women. Many women have a university education. Among men, education is not important. Women know they are superior to men.

X-ian women have become famous for the design and care of flower gardens. In Country X the Queen's Garden is open once a year on her birthday to women only, to celebrate the natural process of growth and rebirth. No foreigners have been able to observe the Queen's Garden Festival, although there is no law to prevent foreigners from attending.

X-ians do not like prolonged eye contact. They look at other people with brief glances during conversation. In Country X, it is very impolite and aggressive to "stare."

You are an X-ian couple. Mrs. and Mr. Alef. Mrs. Alef is the Director of Cultural Affairs. Mrs. Alef is on an official trip to Athens and she has brought her husband along for a brief vacation from his housekeeping duties. You have been seen by a foreign jounalist couple. Mrs. Alef has met them very briefly several years ago.

When speaking English to the foreigners, you must limit your vocabulary to words of only one or two syllables and short simple sentences. You have difficulty comprehending rapid spoken English. Mr. Alef's English is, in fact, very poor. The reason, of course, is that English is a foreign language and you rarely use it at home. You may speak X-ian with each other. The foreign couple will ask for your permission to attend the next Queen's Garden Festival. They will talk to you for about fifteen minutes. Then they will excuse themselves for a few minutes and return to ask permission.

Mrs. Alef must decide to say "yes" or "no." There are three things to consider. Basically, she should decide "yes" if the foreigners have shown cultural sensitivity to what X-ians are like. Look for these things:

1. The foreign woman only must ask for permission and she must ask Mrs. Alef. The men in the role-play must not be involved in the request.

2. You must decide how thoughtful the foreigners have been about your limited English. If they have adjusted their language to your level, this will be one factor in a "yes" decision.

3. The foreigners must also show sensitivity to your custom of little eye contact. If they have "stared" at you during the conversation, your answer should be "no."

Cultural Scene

Briefing Sheet #2

You are two well-known journalists. You are a married couple. Both of you have spent several years in international travel reporting on political, cultural and artistic subjects in a number of countries.

You have just seen two people in a restaurant in Athens. You met them once before very briefly. You do not remember their names, but you do remember they are from Country X, an unusual place seldom visitied by foreigners.

You are aware that Country X is known for its highly developed arts, especially landscape gardens. Once a year there is a great festival called the X-ian Queen's Garden Festival. But no foreigner has actually seen or photographed the festival. It would be a journalistic "coup" if you could do so.

In this exercise, you will approach the X-ians at their restaurant table and ask to join them. Then, after about fifteen minutes find an excuse to leave them. Decide the best way to ask permission to visit the Festival and do a story with photographs.

After your decision is made, return to the table and make your request. You will receive a "yes" or "no" answer.

13.

Family Life

The students observe and participate in a role-play that centers on family life in the U.S.

Objectives

To give the students the opportunity to compare U.S. family life and their own cultures.

To consider techniques that might be helpful in bridging the gap between "outsider" and "member."

Family Life

Procedure

1. Explain to the class that some Americans have been invited to the class to role-play some scenes that might happen in a U.S. family.

   > Prepare your actors to role-play two or three scenes from U.S. family life. Some examples might be: Eating and cleaning up after a meal, spending the evening at home, going out for a meal, going to a party at a friend's house, a visit from the grandparents, etc. Ask the players to be as natural as possible in their speech and behavior. Explain that there will be a foreign guest in the scene. Each scene should be about 10 minutes.

2. Ask one student to volunteer to participate in each of the scenes. Ask the students who are watching to note any new words or expressions they hear.

   > Introduce each scene by telling the students who the characters are and where and when the scene takes place. Explain that the students who volunteer to be part of the scene are foreign visitors to a U.S. family.

   > If you want several students to have the chance to participate in the role-play, you can stop a scene half way through and ask a new student to take over.

3. After the role-play is over, ask the students to meet in small groups and talk about these questions:

   a. What new words or expressions did you hear?

   b. What observations can you make about the family life you saw in the role-plays?

   c. How does this family compare with your own?

   d. How did the "guest" feel in the scenes?

If you do not have enough time, skip this step and go on to Step 4. The reason for having the students meet in small groups first is to allow everyone to make comments.

It would be helpful to give the students a few minutes after each scene to write down their thoughts.

The purpose for the first question is not only to work on vocabulary, but also to get the discussion started. The purpose of the second question is to ask the students to make some observations about U.S. family life and to work on the distinction between observations and interpretation. The last question gives them the opportunity to think about becoming part of a new culture and entering unknown situations.

Synthesis

4. **The entire group discusses the questions in Step 3. Each small group can summarize its answers through a spokesperson.**

    It may be interesting to consider the similarities and differences among the small group summaries.

5. **Ask the students to consider this question:**

    What can you do to become more of a member of the host culture?

14.

Nonverbal Communication

Using short skits, the students explore the nature and importance of nonverbal communication.

Objective

To introduce the students to the nature and importance of nonverbal communication.

To teach some appropriate nonverbal responses and attitudes.

Procedure

1. **Briefly introduce the nature of nonverbal communication.**

   You can use the outline at the end of this lesson as the basis for a short talk to the class. In many cases, the students can supply examples of the kinds of nonverbal signals and behavior in the outline.

   Another kind of introduction is a short role-play. Have a friend come to class to stage a conversation with you. Then ask the class to tell you what they know about the two people (sex, age, relationship) and how they know this. Then lead into a discussion of what nonverbal communication is.

Nonverbal Communication

2. **Explain to the class that everyone will be involved in enacting some short scenes.**

   If the class is multicultural, ask the students to work in their own nationality groups to enact scenes from their own culture, using their own language.

   If the class is monocultural, ask them to work together in two or three small groups to enact scenes from their own culture or from U.S. culture. If you can, invite two or three people from a culture different from your students', and give these visitors the same assignment. This will allow you to have another group as a contrast.

   Within the work groups the students need to determine the appropriate nonverbal behavior for each situation and decide who will enact the situations (encourage all the students to be involved in at least one).

3. **Give the students directions and time enough to prepare.**

   Some scenes that I have used are:

   a. Mother and father greeting a teenage son after a separation of about six months.

   b. Greeting one's grandmother/grandfather.

   c. Two friends of the same age greet each other after one of them returns from having been away.

   d. A friend sharing sad news with another friend.

   Whichever situations are used, allow for male-to-male, female-to-female and mixed interaction.

4. **The students enact the scenes.**

   If you can video-tape the scenes, the tape can be used in the next step.

Nonverbal Communication

5. Ask the students for their observations.

> I ask the students to confine their comments to nonverbal behavior (physical contact, eye contact, distance, facial expressions, etc.).
> You might also want to ask them to comment on the tone and volume of speech of the role-players.

6. Ask the students for their observations of nonverbal communication that they have observed outside of class. Pursue this topic with the following questions:

a. What new nonverbal communication responses have you learned to use comfortably?

b. What new nonverbal communication responses are you comfortable using? Why?

This step will give the students an opportunity to talk about their personal experiences with U.S. culture.

In Question B., it is important to ask "why" because this question will help the students increase their awareness of specific non-verbal behavior in the target culture.

For a photographic catalog of American gestures, see ESL Miscellany, Pro Lingua Associates, pp. 259-170.

Synthesis

7. Summarize by asking the students to write a short definition of nonverbal communication.

AN OUTLINE OF PARALINGUISTIC COMMUNICATION

A. **Sounds**
   1. Individual sounds
      a. fricatives -- Shh!
      b. nasals -- Mmmm.
      c. trills -- Brrr!
      d. clicks and stops -- tsk tsk. Pst!

   2. Emotional intonation
      a. surprise
      b. fear
      c. anger
      d. sarcasm
      e. mockery
      f. complaint
      g. persuasion
      h. flirtation
      i. intimacy
      j. pleasure

   3. Exclamations and interjections

   4. Voice qualities and styles
      a. whisper
      b. baby talk
      c. falsetto

   5. Whistling
   6. Humming
   7. Yelling
   8. Laughing
   9. Crying
  10. Coughing

B. **Body language** (Kinesics)
   1. Facial expressions
   2. Eye contact
   3. Gestures
   4. Touching (Haptics)

C. **Other areas of paralinguistic communication**
   1. Silence
   2. Time
   3. Space and distance (Proxemics)

from ESL Miscellany, Pro Lingua Associates, p. 255.

15.

Empathy

The students read and discuss a short passage in which cultural differences cause a communication problem.

Objectives

> To practice empathy by identifying cultural perspectives.

> To look for ways to improve intercultural communication.

Procedure

1. **The students read a sketch in which there is a difference in cultural perspective.**

> Two examples are given below. Using them as models, you can write one yourself that is more relevant to your students' circumstances. You may want to choose a sketch that involves a culture represented by someone in your class, so that if some culture-specific information is needed in the discussion that follows, it can be given by someone in the group.

Empathy

2. Lead the students in a discussion of the sketch.

These are the questions that I use in leading the discussion:

a. What are _____'s thoughts and feelings about this situation?

b. What are _____'s thoughts and feelings about this situation?

c. What is the problem?

d. What suggestions would you give to _____ for resolving this problem?

e. What suggestions would you give to the other person for resolving this problem?

The purpose of this discussion is to establish the two cultural points of view, to identify the problem or conflict and to make suggestions for improved communication and relationships across cultures. It is helpful to write the students' responses on the board or on large pieces of paper to refer to throughout the discussion.

Synthesis

3. Lead the students in a summary discussion based on the following two questions:

a. What is empathy?

b. Why is it important in intercultural relationships?

Because each sketch involves a different situation and different people, this exercise can be repeated two or three times. Each time, the skill of empathy is being strengthened.

From Webster's New World Dictionary: empathy the projection of one's own personality into the personality of another in order to understand him better; ability to share in another's emotions or feelings.

Empathy

SKETCH

On the Job

Thin Lo, who is from Vietnam, has lived in the U.S. for four years. For the past year and a half, she has been working as an assembly worker for the ACP Electronics Company. Her supervisor is an American named Jim Black.

Thin likes her job and is a very good worker, but she is upset with her supervisor. Jim continues to have weekly meetings with the 12 assembly people in his department. All of them are from Asian countries. He keeps asking them for suggestions for increasing production and for better work conditions. She thinks this is a waste of the company's time because this is the supervisor's job, not the workers' job.

On the other hand, Jim has been increasingly dis-couraged lately. He wants his workers to feel a part of a team. But when he tries to include them by asking for suggestions, usually no one says anything.

SKETCH

At the University

Hiroshi is a junior at a small U.S. university. He studied English for many years in Japan, and now he speaks the language very well. He is a very good student and enjoys most of his classes. But there is one class he is taking this semester that has upset him.

In the class, there are only 14 students, and they are all American except for Hiroshi. They spend most of the class time in discussions led by the professor. Hiroshi wants to drop this course because the students seem impolite and self-centered. They aren't interested in the ideas and opinions of each person because they interrupt and argue with each other. Also, they don't try to reach a group consensus.

The American students in the class are beginning to think that Hiroshi either can't speak English very well or that he doesn't have many ideas because he never says anything in class. They don't want to be rude, but they are starting to ignore him in their discussions.

16.

Interview

Each student interviews a native speaker and then the class compares notes on the information and attitudes expressed during the interviews.

Objective

To look for the similarities and universals that underlie different cultures.

Procedure

1. Hand out the questionnaires and explain to the students that they are to interview a person from the U.S.

   There is a sample questionnaire given at the end of this lesson.

Interview

This interview can be done as homework or during class time. Of course, if it is done during class time, you will have to invite some native speakers to the class. For best results, there should be one student to one native speaker.

Encourage the students to write down the information gathered. This can be done in note form during the interview or immediately following the interview.

It might be helpful if the students each had a small map of the U.S. to take with them on the interview.

2. **After the interviews have been conducted, discuss the information gathered.**

Discuss the questions on the questionnaire one at a time. First ask the students to talk about what their interviewees said. Second, ask the students to compare this information with their own cultures. Encourage the students not to make judgements about one point of view being "better" than another.

Be sure to have a world map in the classroom or an individual map for each country represented in your class.

3. **Ask the students these questions about the interviewing process and the preceding discussion:**

   a. **Were you surprised by anything that the person you interviewed said? What? Why?**

   b. **Was it easy or difficult to answer the questions about your own culture?**

   c. **What did you learn about your ability to communicate in English?**

   While Step 2 is designed to compare cultural information, Step 3 gives the students the opportunity to talk about the process of the interview.

Interview

Synthesis

4. **Hand out and/or read the passage below and ask the students for their reactions to it.**

> Oh, East is East, and West is West, and
>   never the twain shall meet,
> Till Earth and Sky stand presently at God's
>   great Judgement Seat;
> But there is neither East nor West, Border,
>   nor Breed, nor Birth,
> When two strong men stand face to face,
>   tho' they come from the ends of the earth!

The refrain above is from "The Ballad of East and West" by Rudyard Kipling.

QUESTIONNAIRE

1. Where are the concentrations of population in the U.S. and why do people want to live in certain areas and not in others?

2. Why do you live where you do?

3. What is your definition of the good life?

4. What are the two greatest problems facing our world today?

5. What is something positive that has happened in our world in the past year?

17.

Town Survey

The class visits a local community to gather
information. Back in the classroom they share
their information and discuss how they got it.

Objectives

To gather information about a specific community
and how the inhabitants see their own community.

To identify skills and attitudes helpful for entering
and understanding a new culture.

Procedure

1. Explain to the class that they will be going to a
   community to collect some information which will
   be reported back to the rest of the class.

   If your class is located in a city, choose a
   specific area to be investigated. Be sure the
   students are clear about geographical limits.
   You may want to provide each of them with
   a map. I often choose an area the students
   either live in or visit fairly frequently.

   To set the stage, you might want to read the
   excerpt at the end of this lesson.

Town Survey

2. **Show the class a list of categories to be investigated and ask each student to choose a category.**

   Here are some suggested categories: Education, recreation, health services, social services, economic enterprises, government. If you choose to do technique 18, School visit, you may not want to include education among your categories, saving it for the school visit.

   Set a limit on how many students can work with each category. I have found pairs to work well, although sometimes a student may want to work alone. If you are in a large city, different small groups can work on the same category within different geographical areas.

   If you have a culturally mixed class, encourage students from different cultures to work together.

3. **Prepare the students with a list of questions to be asked as they investigate the categories.**

   You can provide them with a questionnaire or, better yet, ask them to frame their own questionnaire. Encourage them to include not only questions that have factual answers, but also questions that will reveal local attitudes and opinions about the community.

4. **Set a time limit for the survey and a specific time to be back in class.**

   A good time span seems to be about three hours. If your class meets only a few hours a week, you can either give this assignment as homework or cancel a couple of your regular classes and have the students do this assignment at a time that is convenient for them.

5. **Tell the students that there will be a five minute report for each of the categories investigated.**

   Remind the students to take some notes during the investigation and encourage them to bring material back with them (brochures, bulletins, pamphlets, etc.).

72

6. After the survey the students plan and give their presentations.

Setting a time limit on presentations is important. It helps the students be concise and keeps the reporting from being long and drawn out. You may want to give the students some suggestions on summarizing the information.

Thirty to forty minutes is usually enough time for the presentations. Encourage the students to display any matieral that has been collected. After the survey, I often leave this material posted in the classroom and try to use it in future lessons.

You can request that all the students in a group give part of the oral report or that the group choose one spokesperson. If two or more small groups have investigated a single category, I would suggest they summarize all their information for just one final report.

Synthesis

7. Pose these questions for discussion:

a. How did you get the information you wanted?

b. What helped you get the information and what did not help very much?

c. **How did you feel about collecting the information?**

d. **When you first arrived in the U.S. did you use any of these same tactics in trying to understand what was happening around you and in trying to understand what you were supposed to do? Did you have any of the same feelings?**

In questions a. and b. you are trying to help the students identify how they gather information in a new situation. The students may not understand what you are asking because the questions seem very simplistic. In question a. for example, the students may respond, "I asked questions." Help them be more specific. You might ask, "Did you first introduce yourself?" "Did you explain the class project as a way of introduction?" "Did you walk into a place and spend a little time observing before going up to talk to someone?" "How did you choose a person to talk to?"

In question b. help the students identify not only their own behavior but their own attitudes as well.

Question c. gives the students an opportunity to talk about what it felt like to meet new people and ask for information and help.

Write up the students' responses to the first three questions so these can be used as a bridge to the final question.

This last question is not meant to be a "yes" or "no" question. Ask it and give the students a chance to think about their responses while re-reading what they have said to the first three questions.

8. **Use the reading below as a conclusion to the exercise if you don't use it in Step 2.**

READING

In the following excerpt the author is in the interior of Brazil. He has just reached his destination and he is telling somebody about his trip.

...I named the hamlet (where I had just come from). "Did they show you the rock marking the center of the world?" he asked. I assured him they had. "My grandfather came from there," he said. "The exact center. Everyone around here has always known about it."

The import of the rock marking the center of the world took a while to filter through. I had initially doubted their claim, knowing for a fact that the center was located somewhere in New England. After all, my grandfather had come from there. But gradually I realized they had a valid belief, a universal concept, and I agreed with them. We tend to define the center as that special place where we are known, where we know others, where things mean much to us, and where we ourselves have both identity and meaning; family, school, town and local region. The lesson which gradually filtered through was the simple concept that every place has special meanings for the people in it; every place represents the center of the world. The number of such centers is incalculable, and no one student or traveler can experience all of them, but once a conscious breakthrough to a second center is made, a life-long perspective and collection can begin.

An excerpt from "The Green Banana" by Donald Batchelder. Beyond Experience, The Experiment Press, Brattleboro, VT., 1977. P. 138.

18.

School Visit

The students visit a school and then discuss their observations.

Objectives

To give the students an opportunity to deepen their understanding of one sociocultural institution -- education in the U.S.

To compare and contrast various educational systems and philosophies.

Procedure

1. **Explain the structure of the U.S. educational system.**

    An example of how this information might be presented visually is given at the end of the lesson. The simpler your explanation, the more helpful it will be in Steps 2 and 3 when the students have to do the same.

2. **Give the students large pieces of paper and ask them to illustrate the educational systems in their countries.**

    If you have more than one student from a particular country, ask them to work together

in drawing the educational systems in their
country. If you have a monocultural class,
have the whole class discuss and agree on
a visual and decide who will draw it.

3. **Ask each student to give a brief explanation
of the system in his country.**

It is important to emphasize to the students
that there will be a definite time limit to
the explanations. I suggest three minutes.
They are not to give details, but they should
follow your example in Step 1. Allow time
after each presentation for others in the
class to ask questions.

If your class is all from one culture, ask the
class to choose a spokesperson. The explanation,
in this case, would be given to you.

4. **Explain the arrangements for the school visit.**

I have found that both elementary and high
schools are very interested in hosting foreign
students. It is helpful if there is one person
at the school who is responsible for making
all the arrangements and for communicating
with you.

There are a variety of ways these visits can
be set up; the following are examples suitable
for high school visits. Each of your students
can be assigned a "buddy" at the host school,
in which case the pair stays together throughout the visit. Or, the contact person at the
school can arrange a schedule for each of
your students, giving them an opportunity
to visit a few different classes.

Sometimes a request is made by language
teachers for your students to be a part of
language classes. This has worked well only
when the students also have an opportunity
to visit other subject matter classes, as well.

In visiting elementary classes, the students
have stayed in one class or have been divided

among a few classes. They have participated
in whatever way the host teacher felt was
suitable.

A high school visit, because of the opportunity to visit a variety of different classes
can last from three hours to an entire
school day. Three hours is a good length of
time for an elementary school visit.

5. **Hand out the observation questions.**

There is a sample guideline given at the
end of the lesson. Go over the questions
to be sure they are clear. These questions
are not meant to be asked directly,
but are to be used as guides in observing.
The exception to this is Question 5.

Synthesis

6. **After the visit, take the questions one at a
time, asking the students to comment on what
they observed, and to compare their observations
with their own educational experiences.**

Before the discussion begins, give the students
a chance to write a few notes about their
observations on each question. It might be
best to first discuss their observations and
then make comparisons. Watch for the
tendency to judge one system over another
or to make broad statements after only
a short visit to one school.

7. **Ask the students to summarize their experience by
thinking or writing about this question:**

**Compare one aspect of the U.S. educational
system with that of your own country. For
this one aspect, what are the strengths and
weaknesses of the two systems.**

OBSERVATION GUIDELINE

1. How would you describe the relationship between

   - teachers and students?

   - students with each other?

2. In what ways (reading, discussion, games, writing, etc.) are the students learning?

3. How would you describe the general atmosphere of the classroom?

4. How do you think the students feel about being in school? Why do you have this opinion?

5. What subjects do the students study? Do they have homework? How much? Do they have tests? How often?

U.S. EDUCATIONAL SYSTEM

Name of School	Grade	Age of Students	Subjects		
Nursery		4	Games, songs, creative playing		
Kindergarten	K	5	Games, drawing, crafts, beginning reading & writing		
Primary or Elementary	1	6	Reading, writing, spelling, adding, drawing, singing		
	2	7	Language arts, subtraction, spelling, drawing, singing		
	3	8	Language arts, social studies, multiplication		
	4	9	Language arts, social studies, division		
	5	10	Language arts, history, geography, fractions		
	6	11	Language arts, history, geography, decimals, science		
Junior High	7	12	Language arts, history, geograhpy, algebra, science, foreign language, manual arts, home economics		
	8	13	Language arts, history, geography, geometry, science, foreign language, manual arts, home economics		
High School			College Prep	Vocational	Business
	9 Freshman	14	English	English	English
	10 Sophomore	15	Math	Economics	Book-
	11 Junior	16	Science	Civics	keeping
	12 Senior	17	Physical	Math	Civics
			Biology	Shop	Math
			Physics	Home	Typing
			Chemistry	Economics	
			Foreign Lang.		
			Spanish		
			French		
Junior College (2 yrs) College or University (4 yrs) (under-graduate)	Freshman	18	English, foreign language, history, biology, physical science, sociology or psychology, physical education, ROTC		
	Sophomore	19			
	Junior	20	Courses in major and minor fields		
	Senior	21			
Graduate or Professional School	MA	22-	One-year plus thesis		
	PhD		Three years plus dissertation		

19.

Cultural Adjustment

Each student identifies stages and changes in his process of adjustment to living in the U.S. The results are shared and discussed.

Objective

> To aid the students in gaining perspective on their process of adjustment to new cultures.

Procedure

1. **The students silently recall their stay in the U.S. from the beginning to the present.**

   > Before beginning the recall, it is helpful to suggest that each person write down the significant events or situations that they remember. Also ask the students to recall the thoughts and feelings they had at various times during the period of their stay. At this point, what they write does not have to be in any kind of order. The purpose of this initial step is to bring alive past experience.

Cultural Adjustment

During the silent recall, you might want to play some background music. Try the first two movements from Dvorak's "New World Symphony."

2. **The students identify the STAGES they have gone through in their adjustment to living in the U.S.**

   This is usually not an easy task, and the students often need guidance. "Stages" are periods when there are attitudes, feelings and behavior that prevail through a period of time.

   Two examples of student responses to this step are given at the end of the lesson. You may want to use these as aids to illustrate the concept of stages. Encourage each student to label each stage with a word or two and to make simple statements that represent the stage. Make crayons, magic markers and large pieces of paper available.

3. **Ask the students to identify what caused the changes in attitude, feelings and behavior from one stage to another.**

   The causes can be summarized in a list. There is a typical student list given at the end of this lesson.

4. **The students meet in small groups to share the stages and changes they identified in Steps 2 and 3.**

   Once this sharing is complete, I often ask all the students to post their work so that everyone will have an opportunity to look at the various responses. I usually ask for any general observations.

   At the time of doing this exercise, the students will probably be at different stages in their adjustment. Some may be at a stage of "acceptance" while others may be "angry" or "lonely". It is valuable to point this out to the class.

Cultural Adjustment

You might want to compare the students' stages of cultural adjustment with the stages of cultural awareness and intercultural adjustment skills outlined in the introduction to this book.

5. **The students discuss in the large group their responses to Steps 2 and 3.**

   Guide the students away from giving detailed accounts of their experiences in Step 3. Some circumstantial explanation may be necessary to explain what caused a change in behavior, feelings and attitude, but help the students be brief and precise. It is very helpful to write these "causes of change" on the board and at the end of the discussion of this step, to ask again for general observations.

   The value of discussing Steps 2 and 3 in the large group is that the participants have the opportunity to hear each others' experiences and to see that <u>adjustment is a process.</u>

Synthesis

6. **Ask the students to answer this summary question:**

   What have you learned about your ability to live in another culture?

   This step can be done orally, but it might be better to give it as a writing assignment.

   To give them some guidance, you could ask them to make their statements in two parts:

   a. What do you do that helps the adjustment process?

   b. What do you do that hinders the adjustment process?

EXAMPLES OF STAGES OF ADJUSTMENT

(Step Two)

STUDENT ONE

Label

Statement

a. interest and excitement

a. "everything is new and interesting"

b. impatience

b. "Why do they have to do things this way?"

c. acceptance

c. "What is right for me may not be right for the other person."

d. questioning

d. "What are my true values?"

e. finding my place

e. "How can I live here and keep my own identity?"

STUDENT TWO

Label

Statement

a. observer

a. "I can learn by watching."

b. confusion

b. "Who am I in this new place?"

c. anger

c. "How can I be myself and live in a place that is so very different?"

STUDENT RESPONSES

To the Question:
What caused the change(s) in attitude and behavior
from one stage to another? (Step Three)

Thinking/reflection

Observation/watching

Asking questions about the new culture and about
about myself

Trying new things

Understanding my own culture

Learning and practicing more language

Time

Learning more about U.S. culture

Acceptance

Contact with people

Desire to learn and adapt

Empathy

Identifying my values

Being nonjudgemental

20.

Summing Up

The students summarize their intercultural experiences in writing and discuss the next phase of their lives.

Objectives

> To give the students the opportunity to summarize their intercultural experience and learning.

> To help the students prepare for the next step-- staying on or going home.

Procedure

1. **Hand out a set of study questions and ask the students to write their responses.**

> Hand out the questions a few days before you plan to have the class discussion, and ask that each question be answered in writing. Go over each question with the students to be sure they understand what is being asked.

> Two samples are included below--one for students who are going to return to their own countries and one for students who are going to stay in the U.S.

Summing Up

2. Ask the students to share their responses to each question.

> The structure of this exercise is fairly simple, but the nature of the questions and the students' personal responses will allow for an in-depth discussion. I have found that students generally appreciate an opportunity to speak about their frustrations and successes.
> Because of the personal nature of the questions, though, the students should always be given the option of not answering in a large group. Sometimes there may be a hesitation to begin, but after the first few people have spoken, almost everyone will want to offer something from his own experience.

Synthesis

3. Ask each student to describe the next step (staying on, going home, new job, etc.) he is going to take and what he expects to be easy and difficult.

> You might also want to take this opportunity to have the students evaluate the techniques you have used.

4. Ask the students to read and reflect on the quote from Gandhi at the end of this technique.

Summing Up

QUESTIONS FOR STUDENTS REMAINING IN THE U.S.

1. What is the biggest adjustment you have had to make living in the U.S.

2. What are the most valuable aspects of your own culture?

3. What aspects of U.S. life are you interested in adopting?

4. What aspects of American culture have you found the hardest to live with?

5. What aspects of American culture have you most enjoyed?

6. What have been important things you have learned about your culture since you have come to the U.S.?

7. What do you miss the most about your native country?

8. If friends of yours were moving to the U.S., what would you tell them about this culture that might help them in their adjustment?

QUESTIONS FOR STUDENTS RETURNING HOME

1. What's the biggest adjustment you have had to make during your stay in the U.S.?

2. What are the most valuable aspects of your own culture that you would be unwilling to give up?

3. What aspects of American life would you be willing to adopt if you were staying in the U.S. now instead of returning home.

4. What aspects of American culture have you found the hardest to live with?

5. What aspects of American culture have you most enjoyed?

6. Do you think you will take anything of the U.S. culture back with you?

   What?

   Why?

7. What have been the two most important things you have learned about your culture?

8. What will be difficult about your return home?

9. What do you think you will remember most about your experience living in the U.S.?

"I do not want my house to be walled in on all sides and my windows to be stuffed. I want the cultures of all lands to be blown about my house as freely as possible. But I refuse to be blown off my feet by any."

—*Mahatma Gandhi*

Medical facilities on the Navajo Indian Reservation, 1966–67

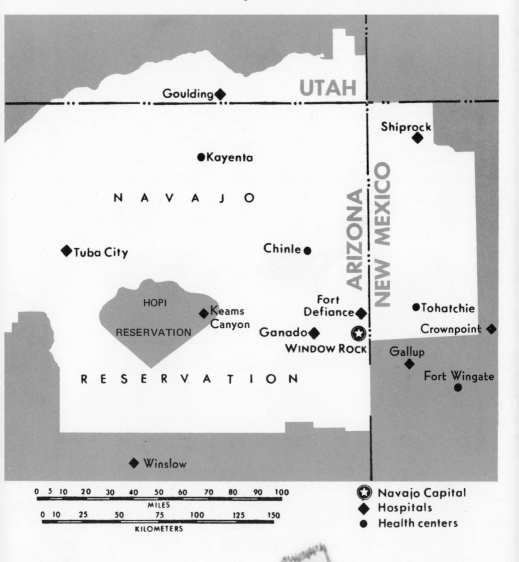

FEDERAL HEALTH CARE

(With Reservations!)

Robert L. Kane
Rosalie A. Kane

Springer Publishing Company, Inc., New York

Cover photo by Mark Rindflesh

For Our Parents

Harold and Ruth Kane
and
Maxwell and Pearl Smolkin

Acknowledgments

We are grateful for the stimulation provided by many of the physicians and staff members at the Shiprock Hospital during 1969 and 1970. The enthusiasm and willingness to innovate which was present in all departments made our experience in Shiprock an exciting one and generated the approaches described in this book. We hesitate to identify these numerous individuals by name lest inclusion jeopardize their positions or accidental omission jeopardize our friendships.

The Community Health Representatives at Shiprock were extremely helpful in interpreting the community, assessing consumer attitudes, and giving us a Navajo point of view. Similarly we are grateful to Dr. and Mrs. Taylor McKenzie who shared their valuable insights with us. The opinions, suggestions, and criticisms, however, are those of the authors and we assume responsibility for their sometimes abrasive quality.

Students are invariably a source of help and stimulation to their preceptors. We thank all the students in various disciplines who were at Shiprock during our tenure. In particular, we thank Peter Rudd, John Jacoby and Lynne Oakland, for both the studies they conducted and the ideas they generated.

Kurt Deuschle, Howard Brown, Peter Rudd, and William M. Wilson reviewed the manuscript at various stages. We are grateful for their interest and suggestions, while recognizing that the end-product does not necessarily reflect their views.

Finally, we thank Betty Byrne who patiently typed and retyped the manuscript and Pearl Smolkin whose grasp of syntax, grammar, and orthography was of great assistance during the proof reading process.

We wish to thank the following for permission to print copyrighted material in this book: Bodley Head, Ltd.; Thomas Brod; *The Chicago Sun-Times; Dine Baa-Hani;* John E. Jacoby; Taylor McKenzie; The Macmillan Company; W. W. Norton & Company; George A. Silver; *The Nation.* Full citations are given in the chapters in which the copyrighted material appears. The map of the Navajo Reservation which appears on the front endpaper is from Brown et al, The Epidemiology of Accidents Among the Navajo Indians, *Public Health Reports 85:* 883, October, 1970.

Salt Lake City,   Robert L. Kane,
August, 1971   Rosalie A. Kane

Foreword

Dr. and Mrs. Kane have written a fascinating study of the Indian Health Service, a multimillion-dollar federal health care system serving a deprived population. Their analysis has particular relevance now for the debate on the adoption of national health insurance.

Impatient, unaccepting of the injustices of the health system they write about, the Kanes typify the best of the new breed of young professionals. As reactions by activists, the book is well worth reading. However, it offers more. It is one of the very few studies that have been done of large bureaucratic systems of health. Most previous studies have dealt only with hospitals, and it shows, with clarity and fairness, the strengths and weaknesses of a large bureaucratic health service.

For the Kanes, "community medicine is the identification of health problems in communities and the search for solutions to these problems." Looking at their given Navajo community from this vantage point, they tried first to understand the social, political, economic, and geographic factors that related to the health of that community. Dr. Kane's attempts to implement some of the changes he proposed are detailed in this book, as are his thoughts on the overall problems of bureaucratically-administered health services. The authors describe the prerequisites for what they call "the change-seeking spirit," and offer suggestions for avoiding the obvious evils of the present system. They discuss the problems of measurements for effective health programs. These are yet to be developed. They point out the weakness of over-centralization in the organization of a health system.

No Western nation outside of the United States has a centrally directed and operated health service. In no other Western nation do physicians work for the central government. The British National Health Service, for example, is managed by many regional and local committees, with only a minimal role reserved for the central government, and a similar dispersion of power to local levels can be found in other European countries.

New York City, for example, has an elaborate network of hospitals and health centers operated by the city government. Its highly centralized system and its nonprofessional staff is under civil service, analogous to the Indian Health Service. Many of the problems that the Kanes describe exist also in the New York system, whose difficulties stem in part from lack of dispersion of authority and from rigidity of government operation. This system, like the Indian Health Service, mostly serves the poor, who have not been very

v

effective advocates for better services. As one observes the New York City system, one recognizes a problem that is centrally dealt with in the Kanes' book—the lack of initiative which may be a characteristic trait of those who choose to work in the system, or a quality resulting from the system itself.

There are further parallels between the Indian Health Service and the health services of New York City. In working with local communities that were attempting to set up hospital advisory and operating boards, it has been my experience that local leaders, usually aspiring politicians, take over such boards. They do not exactly block communication with others, but insist that *they* must be the intermediaries, just as the Kanes describe the Indian chiefs as doing. As another example, the Kanes tell us that when the Indians were consulted, they asked for a larger hospital rather than for ambulatory services for which there was a much greater need. Precisely this has happened in New York City communities with which I have worked. In giving priority to hospital size over ambulatory care services, both Indian and urban consumers made the same misjudgment so often made also by the professionals.

In my opinion, all this would seem to suggest that centrally directed bureaucratic systems are not a suitable organizational form for health care delivery. Few professionals in this country realize the extent to which Western Europe has avoided centralized systems. Perhaps, with the advent of National Health Insurance, the Indian Health Service should be replaced by locally controlled services. Local boards could be composed of tribal leaders, similar to the membership of the boards of voluntary hospitals. While not representative, this board structure works fairly well in many areas of the country.

The Kanes have written a good book. I admired them as students, and I respect them even more as teachers, authors, and innovators.

HOWARD J. BROWN, M.D.
Professor of Preventive Medicine,
School of Medicine;
Professor of Public Administration,
School of Public Administration,
New York University

Introduction

On June 25, 1970, the Redding (Calif.) *Record Searchlight* carried an unusual piece of medical news;

> Richard Oakes' fever hit 106. His pulse was irregular. The 28-year-old Mohawk's body shook on his hospital bed in San Francisco.
>
> Then, as skeptical doctors stood by, Mad Bear placed an ancient and secret Indian medicine in the tube that fed the young activist.
>
> Oakes responded within five minutes and within an hour, says Mad Bear, his temperature was normal, his pulse regular and his body relaxed.
>
> Doctors at San Francisco General Hospital admit there was a positive response Monday to the Indian medicine.
>
> Mad Bear, a smile playing on his massive, creased face, recalled that doctors felt the trio was "just fooling around" when they asked permission to treat Oakes. They were allowed to administer the medicine, he said, because Oakes' condition was such that, "what harm could we do?." The doctors say it was Oakes' religious right to be administered the Indian "herbs."
>
> Mad Bear refuses to say what was placed in the teaspoon of medicine placed in the intravenous tube.

Richard Oakes' illness, which kept him hovering on the brink of death during two weeks of coma, was as dramatic in onset as in cure. Mr. Oakes, a leader of the Alcatraz Indian Movement, is also a leader of the Pit River Indians, who are pressing claims for the return of stolen California land. Because of his activities in the second capacity, he was attacked and almost beaten to death with a pool cue in a bar in San Francisco.

Richard Oakes was injured in an Indian cause and, appropriately, his recovery was brought about by an Indian medicine.

Fortunately, the physicians in charge were willing to cede the patient's "religious right" to the medicine. Perhaps they were also aware that medicine men are often skilled in the use of curing herbs. This instance is a clear-cut example of a happy blending of white and Indian medical practices. The intravenous tube of the modern hospital was used to convey the secret, potent drug to the patient!

In the usual, less dramatic course of events, particularly on Indian reservations, sick Indians receive treatment from Indian Health Service physicians in Indian Health Service facilities. In such settings one might expect a synthesis of white and Indian medicine on a routine basis. Unfortunately, the end product would probably not be claimed by either culture as a credit to its medical systems. Too many health problems are unsolved and, worse, almost unattacked. And too many patients have bitter feelings about their dealings with the Indian Health Service.

In 1969 the staggering sum of $112,506,000 was appropriated by Congress for use by the Indian Health Service. This multimillion dollar operation is charged with a mission to "provide comprehensive health care to Indian and Alaskan native people." In the ringing words of the *Program Report and Plan, Indian Health Service, Fiscal Years 1971-1975,* the Service goals are as follows:

> to raise the health level of the Indian and Alaskan native people to the highest possible level; to reduce the mortality and morbidity of Indians by providing expanded and improved preventive health services and treatment of disease and by improving the environment in which the Indians and Alaska natives live, and to accomplish these goals using Indian involvement and participation to the fullest possible extent.

The Indian Health Service employs approximately 5,900 people and spends one hundred twelve million dollars annually, but these goals elude its grasp.

The first author of this book entered the United States Public Health Service in the Indian Health Service division in 1969. His assignment was Service Unit director of the Shiprock Service Unit, an area which encompassed 5,000 square miles and served about 25,000 Navajo Indians. The author was what is known colloquially as a "two-year man"; he had been in the Public Health Service Commissioned Officer Corps as a reservist and was now fulfilling a two-year military obligation.

Presumably the charge of the Service Unit director was to implement the overall goals of the Indian Health Service, as stated above, in the more limited context of the single Service Unit. We quickly perceived a series of impediments in the way of reaching these objectives. Many of the obstacles seemed inherent in the medical system.

The author is a physician with a background in Community Medicine. By training and experience, he was obliged to consider the community he was serving as a total entity and to try to understand the social, political, economic, and geographic factors which were related to the health of that community. From such a perspective, a discrepancy emerged between the stated goals of the Indian Health Service as expressed in its central publications and the effects of the program in practice at a local level.

Of all the factors which impinge on the health of the Service Unit residents, the agency of which we were a part, the Indian Health Service itself, has probably received the least scrutiny. Yet at times the culture of the Indian Health Service seemed as exotic and complex as that of any Indian group. In the following chapters, we will examine the operation of a single Service Unit within the Indian Health Service. From a service-level perspective, we will discuss problems in recruitment and retention of personnel, consumer involvement, satisfaction of both consumer and employee, and response to the challenges of changing health problems. Throughout we are attempting to understand what makes a medical system resistant to change and, more importantly, to describe conditions that facilitate innovative attitudes.

The second author of the book, the wife of the Service Unit director, is a social worker by profession and, at the time of writing, a housewife by necessity. Ironically, the inability of the understaffed Indian agency bureaucracies to utilize part-time personnel afforded her the leisure to help write this book.

Having described what we are, we must emphasize what we are not. Neither author is a historian nor an anthropologist, and our observations are not offered as a description of Navajo society. Usually our examples are drawn from the Navajo reservation and most often from our own particular Service Unit. Our primary purpose, however, is not to document inadequacies in the health care of Indians, but to point up problems within the medical system providing that care. Admittedly the line between these two areas is hazy—as we criticize the producer, we are apt to criticize the product.

Lest we appear to be embarking on an exposé, we should state at the outset that the Indian Health Service has many positive achievements to its credit in its 16-year existence as part of the Public Health Service. Statistics are available, for example, to prove its accomplishments in terms of morbidity and mortality rates, infant mortality, declining disease entities, numbers of added facilities and dollars spent. Although we may dwell on negative aspects of the organization, we do not wish to make a wholesale indictment.

Hidden away beneath a jumble of initials,* the Indian Health Service (IHS) is not often recognized for its unique role. Bureaucratically it is a part of the Health Services and Mental Health Administration (HSMHA) of the Department of Health, Education and Welfare (DHEW). The IHS/HSMHA/ DHEW is the only health program currently federally funded and federally staffed which attempts to provide comprehensive health care to a population.

The large bulk of federal health money does not go for direct service programs. Much is used to support research and medical education (mainly through the National Institutes of Health). Large portions are allotted to states as categorical or block grants to support such programs as tuberculosis control, venereal disease control, maternal and child health projects, or local health department activities. Other funds go into matching monies for health

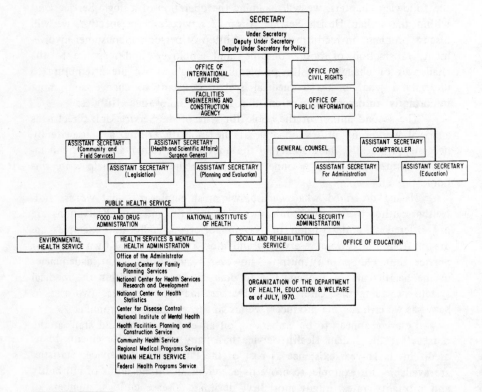

*A glossary of acronyms and organizational terms will be found at the end of this book.

facilities construction and into financing the Federal Drug Administration.

The federal government is also in the business of direct medical care. Most of its programs, however, like those run by the Department of Defense for military personnel and their dependents are limited in scope, stressing clinical services. The Veteran's Administration system is primarily designed for those who have suffered service-connected disabilities. It makes no claim to offer comprehensive care. The Public Health Service (PHS) does have other medical programs but they are all much more restrictive in scope than Indian Health. Services at PHS hospitals are generally limited to curative medicine for specific groups such as merchant marines or PHS personnel. The PHS also provides medical care for federal prisons, but this too is restricted in spectrum.

More recently the federal government, through the Office of Economic Opportunity (OEO) has supported a series of neighborhood health centers. These are generally managed by a local group—either a medical school, another medical institution, or a corporation especially chartered for funding. Moreover the responsibility for truly comprehensive health services is variable. Rarely are such items as environmental health included.

Thus, the Indian Health Service occupies a unique position in the medical care history of the United States. It seems appropriate to examine this agency's experiences with the hope of learning from its successes and failures. The Indian Health Service represents the federal government's most ambitious effort at supplying health care to a civilian population. To ignore the problems in this vast medical care network is to by-pass a unique opportunity to study a centrally-organized federal care system and to observe its effects at the patient level.

Such considerations are timely. It is increasingly clear that current solutions to the demands for affordable medical care are unsatisfactory. A National Health Service Corps for poverty areas has been authorized by Congress. Our reason for writing this book stems from a belief that the Indian Health Service, as a system, should be studied carefully as a prelude to embarking on the inevitable course of newer and perhaps bigger federal health plans.

Contents

Chapter I
Treaty and Treatment

Most Indians and white men believe that the United States government is obligated to provide a measure of health care to the Indian. At the same time, many enlightened commentators believe that the federal government is obligated to provide health care to all its citizens who could not otherwise foot the bill.

Obviously, the Indian has the same "right to health" as any other American. Beyond this moral persuasion, however, the Indians may have a prior claim. It is often assumed that the Indian has a right to medical care under treaties arrived at many decades ago.

Our attempts to become acquainted with the treaties and documents spelling out the agreements between the Navajos and the federal government concerning health care have been frustrating. We can neither confirm nor deny the suspicion that perhaps patients have grounds for a suit against the government for failure to fulfill treaty obligations. The question seems shrouded in mystery.*

Over a hundred years ago, the Navajos lost their last rounds in the struggle against the American government. From 1846, when the United States acquired the Southwestern territories from Mexico, a period of conflict with Navajo bands ensued. But in 1863, Kit Carson instituted a concerted and fearsome campaign against the Navajo. Beginning in the spring of 1864, the conquered Navajos were rounded up at Fort Defiance, New Mexico, and forced to march 360 miles to a new reserve which was being established south of Santa Fe. Nearly a quarter of the people died from malnutrition and infectious diseases in the course of the infamous Long March to Fort Sumner. Finally, in 1868 a treaty was concluded which allowed the remaining Navajos

---

* A more complete examination of the legal issues involved has been prepared in mimeographed form by F. David Grabill, California Indian Legal Services, UCLA School of Law, Los Angeles, California 90024 ("Legal Aspects of Indian Health Problems," June, 1970).

1

"IT SAYS: 'CAUTION—SMOKING MAY BE HAZARDOUS TO YOUR HEALTH.'"

to return to their former homes. A reservation was established straddling New Mexico and Arizona. From time to time, Congress has increased the boundaries of that reservation area.

The treaty signed at Fort Sumner ushered in the beginning of the Navajo reservation as we know it today. The treaty promised the Navajos a school, a blacksmith shop, a warehouse, a chapel, an agency office, and some initial support to begin farming. No provision was made for medical care. The United States had committed itself to support the mind and soul but not the flesh of the Navajo. Seemingly, the "health" was omitted from today's troika, "health, education, and welfare."

In the Navajo case medical care was not covered in the treaty of 1868. Yet many treaties have been conducted between the various tribes and the federal government, as broken promises or misunderstandings have led to new negotiations and further settlements. Some agreements do introduce the principle of health care. By now the documents are confused and inconsistent. The legal foundation on which to base a centralized health program embracing all Indian and Alaskan native people is unsettled.

Nevertheless, the Indian tribes did agree to give up title to the majority of their lands in exchange for a protected trusteeship status. Perhaps in 1868 health care was not envisaged as one of the privileges of civilized society which should have been included along with chapel, school, and blacksmith shop. But the nature of the paternalistic relationship was understood by the white agents of the federal government on the various reservations. This paternalism was extended to embrace health care as a response to events rather than as a planned principle.

Throughout the last century the government apparently has not been clear itself about the extent of its responsibility for Indian health. The confusion is pointed up in a book entitled *Federal Indian Laws* (1) which recounts the government's role in Indian medical care. At the outset the federal government recognized some responsibility for health, concurrent with its responsibility for education. Early appropriations were made from funds authorized for education and were distributed among religious and philanthropic organizations already at work among Indian tribes. One assumes, then, that the original efforts were both underfunded and inconsistent—qualities which still plague the more sophisticated Indian health programs today.

When the War Department controlled Indian affairs, the Indians lived in the vicinity of military posts. It was convenient for the medical care and sanitary regulations to be handled by Army medical personnel stationed nearby. As early as 1832 (while the Army still waged wars against many tribes), Congress appropriated money to enable the Secretary of War to begin a vaccination program for the Indians.

In 1849 the Department of the Interior was established and the existing medical care passed into civilian control. The responsible agency became the Bureau of Indian Affairs (BIA):

Under this department, it is said, agency physicians on the reservation at first gave little attention to the Indians and acted more in the capacity of doctors for government employees, or in connection with Indian schools. Treaties entered into included provisions for physicians and hospitals. In 1873, measures were taken towards furnishing organized medical facilities and an educational and medical division which continued until 1877. By 1874 about one-half of the Indian agencies were each supplied with a physician. After 1878, physicians on Indian reservations were required to be graduates of medical colleges. Between 1880 and 1890 several hospitals were established. In 1909, prevalence of trachoma among the Indians had become so devastating that funds were appropriated for investigations, treatment and prevention of this disease, and in 1912 money was allotted to the Public Health and Marine Service for a survey of trachoma and tuberculosis.

After 1911, appropriations under the heading "Relief of distress and prevention of contagious diseases" were greatly increased and spent on correspondingly increased medical care and hospital facilities. Since 1921 when the Bureau of Indian Affairs was authorized to expend funds for the conservation of health, funds have been specially appropriated for that purpose. In 1924, a special division of health was established in the Office of Indian Affairs (2).

Gradually the BIA seemed to evolve a principle of responsibility for Indian health, until a special division was finally established seventy-five years after the Bureau came into existence.

The next major administrative change in the Indian health programs came about in 1955 as a result of hearings on the health status of the Indian. In that year, responsibility for health was shifted from BIA to the United States Public Health Service, an agency within the Department of Health, Education, and Welfare. The charge to PHS was no less vague than that to BIA had been. The BIA had been directed to take measures "for the relief of distress and conservation of health." PHS was simply instructed to assume "all functions, responsibilities, authorities and duties. . . relating to the maintenance and operation of hospital and health facilities for Indians and the conservation of the health of the Indians."

Returning to the Navajo tribe in the days after the treaty of 1868, we find the people suffering many inconsistencies at the hands of the white federal government. At the same time as the government was gradually getting involved in health services on Indian reservations, other activities were laying the foundation of suspicion which plagues Indian Health Service programs today. Reservation lands were gradually enlarged and then withdrawn or exchanged for less desirable acreage in order to satisfy the covetous railroad interests. Although they held title to their land, the Navajo were exploited by arrangements to extract their valuable mineral resources. Oil, uranium, natural gas, and water were harvested with little or no payment to the Navajo owners. The Navajo were encouraged to develop livestock as an economic base and were then chastised and penalized when overbreeding threatened the already limited grasslands. Successive waves of Anglo bureaucrats introduced, changed, and withdrew ideas for procedures in farming, housing, and health practices. In the latter sphere, breast feeding was first condemmed as barbaric and discouraged, only to be reintroduced as infant malnutrition worsened in the face of an inadequate milk supply and lack of refrigeration.

All this time the federal government was getting deeper into the health field. As we have seen, much of the early activity was a response to critical need. The Navajo did not escape these medical rescue missions. In the early twenties public attention was drawn to the grave problems of trachoma among American Indians. The disease was most menacing in the Southwest among the Navajo and Pueblo tribes. Congress gallantly loosened the pursestrings for a dramatic campaign against trachoma which was launched in 1924 on the Navajo reservation—a special Congressional grant of $100,000 made it possible.

The trachoma campaign is well described by Lawrence Kelly in his recent book *The Navajo Indians and Federal Indian Policy* (3). It is the story of good intentions gone astray. The ill-fated trachoma effort depended on a radical operation on the upper eyelid, a delicate surgical procedure which was still largely unproven. However, it was assumed that the slower method of repeated applications of copper-sulphate was unworkable with an Indian population.

> Despite the fact that the theory was unproved and the tarsectomy operation itself a radical and delicate one, the Indian Bureau issued regulations ordering all its physicians, surgeons or not, to familiarize themselves with the tarsectomy to the end that "every physician in the Indian Service shall be a trachoma specialist." The result was disastrous, particularly in the Southwest where the greatest effort was made. Thousands of operations were performed on Indians, many of whom did not require the radical treatment, many others of whom because of faulty diagnosis did not even have the disease. Some of the physicians who performed the operations were improperly or insufficiently trained in the intricacies of the operation (4).

The operations continued, despite lack of proof that they were effective, until 1927 when they were discontinued, again by central decree. At that point the BIA decided to return to the older medicinal procedure and to place all children with trachoma in a special school where they could readily be treated by a qualified nurse. The children with trachoma were removed to a school at Fort Defiance; the parents of these children were not notified of the change. Such tactics did no good to BIA's health or education establishment in the eyes of the Navajo.

In 1955, when the Public Health Service took over the health administration, numerous problems remained on the Navajo reservation. The BIA had left a heritage of inadequate facilities and understaffed programs. In its last years, the BIA health program was hard put to fill its vacancies with even modestly qualified personnel. Infectious diseases, including tuberculosis and trachoma (remaining even after the heroic campaign of the twenties), were rampant. Immunization levels were very low. Dental care or mental health treatment was virtually unavailable.

In addition, the life-style of the Navajo did not simplify the task of providing medical care. The Navajo were widely scattered over desolate country connected by few roads of any description. The population density averaged only 1.5 persons per square mile. Modern conveniences such as water, electricity, and telephone communication were unavailable. Trading posts dotting the reservation constituted the Navajo's primary contact with the outside world. The median education level in 1947 was less than one year of schooling. At that time about 10 percent of the Navajo population on the reservation was principally or entirely dependent on welfare for subsistence.

The new Indian Health Service administration rose to the challenge with a concerted attack on health problems among Indians. Soon statistics on mortality and morbidity reflected the vigorous efforts of the agency.

The transfer of responsibility from BIA to PHS provided no magic which could suddenly transform a sorry mess into a nation's pride. But PHS did have one concrete advantage. Congress had recently provided that service in the Commissioned Officer Corps of the Public Health Service could be accepted as an alternative to military service in other branches of the Armed Forces. The manpower problems of the Indian Health Service were thus relieved, particularly the problem of obtaining highly qualified professional personnel.

A change process had begun in 1955 which made PHS's task a little easier among the Navajo. Many Navajos had served in the Second World War and, through military service, had been exposed to a new way of life including a system of organized medical care. Then, in medicine itself, new tools were becoming available. Some innovations were impressive even to a people who were wary of the white man and his ways. Penicillin was particularly potent in attacking the diseases of the Navajo. Literally overnight, a shot of an antibiotic could reverse the downward course of a child stricken with otitis or pneumonia. This dramatic treatment successfully mustered converts to the white man's medicine; in later years the patients demanded "shots" for almost all complaints, even those which do not respond to antibiotics.

The new Indian Health Service was perfectly able to fit into and expand upon a hierarchial organization. It is a paramilitary service with a chain of command which extends from Washington down to the health outposts. Land management areas were grouped around the hospitals inherited from the BIA to form Service Units. A series of Service Units was directed from an Area office, and the Area offices, in turn, were responsible to the director of the Indian Health Service. Eventually the chain of authority extends through the ranks of the Department of Health, Education and Welfare until it reaches the cabinet secretary of HEW at the top.

Essentially the organization has retained this shape up to the present, although new Service Units and even additional Area offices have been formed. In many parts of the country a Service Unit consists of the population of an entire tribe with the Area comprising several tribes. From 1955 to 1967 the Service Units on the Navajo reservations were administered out of the Albuquerque Area office. This Area also included the Pueblo tribes and the Mountain Utes (both traditional enemies of the Navajo) as well as several other groups.

Even in 1955, however, the Navajo tribe was by far the most populous of the Indian and Eskimo groups. In 1967 a new Area office was created at Window Rock, Arizona, to administer to the Navajo Service Units. The Window Rock Area is now one of the largest Area operations in terms of population served. It oversees the health programs for the Navajo, which are operated out of eight Service Units covering the 100,000 square miles of the reservation. Shiprock is one of these Service Units.

This elaborate structure is a far cry from the makeshift operations in the early days of Army and BIA administration. It seems certain that the federal government is committed to remaining in the field of Indian health. Still, nobody, neither patients nor providers of care, knows for a certainty whether the vast Indian health system is the result of a legal treaty obligation, a voluntary reparation for a past wrong, or a mere happenstance.

The question is more than academic. The answer determines what redress, if any, the consumers can expect from the system. It determines what controls the consumers may exert over the organization.

Although the treaty obligation, especially in the Navajo case, is not clear, the special status of the Indian is recognized. The original treaties were agreements between sovereign powers. Indian tribes were guaranteed continuing rights to reservation lands and collective existence in return for relinquishing their claims to the greater continent. There is no analogous situation in the United States today. The goal of the Indian Health Service cannot be limited to the provision of quality medical care; that care must be provided in a context which preserves the right of the Indian to his own group identity and life on his own land.

The right to protected reservation status has been challenged in recent history. In the Eisenhower administration, certain legislators perceived the solution of the Indian problem as a policy of "termination." By termination they meant that the Indians would be transformed into equal citizens in a lump sum settlement of all claims against the federal government.* In return the Indians would lose their special status as federal wards and receive only the services of their respective state and local governments. The experiment was a disaster for the tribes who were urged into it and for the local governments. Ill-prepared, the Indians floundered. Economic collapse of previously self-sustaining economies demanded huge welfare subsidies from the localities. The program was not urged on other tribes but the memory remains as a threat. Treaty rights have been ignored in the past by assimilationists who find it absurd for one part of the nation's citizenry to sign a treaty with another. Indians know that if they urge an issue on the basis of treaty rights, they risk reviving all the old arguments which brought about the termination policy.

To some extent medical care for Indians is recognized as a right by the federal government. Tribal leaders are expected to become spokesmen for the health needs of their communities. But the government itself is the final critic and judge of its own health system—a convenient but illogical situation.

Eventually the matter will be resolved in the United States courts. Whether the obligation to provide medical care to Indians is a legal one, a moral one which has taken on legal force, or no obligation at all will be interpreted by the judges. Until then, the consumers do not know where they stand with their health system.

The status of Indians is unique and their "right to health" is founded on premises which cannot be applied to other groups, such as migrant workers,

---

* In point of fact the Citizenship Act of 1924 had bestowed full rights as American citizens upon Indians without jeopardizing their additional rights as Indian people.

Appalachian poor, or urban blacks. Most assuredly these groups also have distinct health needs which are not being met and which may require special institutions to handle, but none of them have been guaranteed a protected status in exchange for territorial concessions. The Indian tribes, on the other hand, have made these agreements and cannot be expected to merge into the American mainstream against their will. In a sense, those who choose to remain on the reservations have been guaranteed a separate solution to their health problems.

While the Indian situation is not typical of federal health programs in the past nor of those likely to be adopted in the future, this question of "right to service" does have wider implications. The terms of the contract between the provider and consumer of medical care should be mutually understood, and the degree of obligation should be delineated. Every medical system requires a mechanism for independent criticism, whether the critic be the consumer or some third party.

The other ventures of the federal government into the medical arena are freer of these problems. The Defense Department's health program for military dependents is clearly defined as a fringe benefit and is understood as part of the remuneration for employee services. If the system becomes intolerable, the recipient may terminate his federal employment. Similarly, the Veterans Administration system is seen as a fulfillment of an obligation which the government owes to those who served the country. The scope and limitations of its activities are meticulously defined. Moreover, veterans constitute a powerful political force capable of lobbying to keep the agency serving their needs.

The neighborhood health centers of OEO, on the other hand, contain a built-in mechanism for consumer control. Theoretically, the boards of directors, a majority of whom are consumers, determine policy. In reality the mechanism seldom works. The direction of neighborhood health centers was and is controlled more by political exigencies than any boards. In Moynihan's term, "maximum feasible misunderstanding" has ensued. One misunderstanding is the matter of obligation—these programs which were designed to assure "rights to health" can be dissolved or reduced on the decision of local or central governments. The only reaction left to many confused consumers has been anger.

Unlike OEO neighborhood health centers, the Indian Health Service has been providing some measure of health services for at least a hundred years. As we have shown, the services sprang up piecemeal as responses to particular problems and as a recognition that health is inexorably linked to well-being.

Accountability to the patient has hardly been considered. In the private sector, one can change one's physician. On the Indian reservations there are few private doctors. The Indian must accept the care offered or buy outside care despite his conviction that he is entitled to government medical services.

On the Navajo reservation, the educational system has lately been held to account by the Navajo people. In a few districts, the Navajos have assumed control of the schools and curriculum despite the fact that the funding is still federal and most of the teachers are still white. Some accountability must also be expected in the medical system. The health professions are challenged by the necessity of relinquishing control while improving the quality of health care.

REFERENCES

1. *Federal Indian law*. U.S. Government Printing Office, 1958.
2. *Ibid.*, pp 282-283.
3. Kelly, L. *The Navajo Indians and federal Indian policy*. Tucson: University of Arizona Press, 1968.
4. *Ibid.*, pp. 185-186.

Chapter II

Dissatisfaction Guaranteed

If one set out to design a health system which would be assured of failure, what might be the prime ingredients?

1. The medical care should be offered in a form which is not highly valued by the consumer.
2. The providers and the consumers should be unable to communicate.
3. The providers should represent a system which has a history of unjust and inconsistent dealings with the consumers.
4. The providers should remain with the consumers for no more than a few years lest they become too familiar with their ways.
5. The administration of the medical care system should rest as much as possible at a centralized level away from the scene of delivery. It should stress uniformity of procedure despite local differences in need.
6. Funding should not be related to local needs and conditions but rather should encourage maximum volume of services regardless of quality.

The Indian Health Service, which renders health care to the Navajo, contains all of these elements. Some of the factors are a legacy of history, in which case the Indian Health Service is not responsible for the condition but is faced with the challenge of minimizing it. Other factors are a direct result of PHS administrative structure. Taken together, they describe a health system with built-in obstacles.

First, the medical care is offered in a form which is not highly valued by the consumer. Traditional Navajo medicine classifies the practices of the white physician at the lowest level.

The Navajo religion is a closed system based on mythology into which

11

all phases of life are incorporated. Harmony is the ultimate good, and health or well-being requires a preservation of the prescribed order. Sickness is any disruption of the state of harmony, be it physical, mental, social or environmental in nature. Disharmony is created in two ways: 1) transgression of prescribed behavior, that is violation of a taboo, or 2) witchcraft. Treatment of the symptom or its etiology must be sought from the appropriate practitioner among the hierarchy.

The Singer is the high priest in the Navajo religion. He alone has the ability to cure illness, that is, to restore the individual to a state of harmony. He does not deign to provide symptomatic treatment, nor to set bones or attend women at childbirth. Through elaborate and obssessively precise ceremony, the Singer rectifies the transgression or removes the spell. The ceremonies are long (often more than a week), involving intense interactions between the practitioner and the patient. No history is taken and no physical examination is performed. Often the patient's family and friends are active participants. The fees are quite high (as befits a practitioner who has studied over five years to learn his skill), and in addition the patient must bear the attendant costs of feeding and housing guests.

The second-ranking practitioner in the Navajo hierarchy is the diagnostician. Since the Singer does not make a diagnosis, the diagnostician must ascertain the etiology of the disease in order to recommend the appropriate specialist. In contrast to the Singer, the diagnostician undergoes no extended apprenticeship. Instead he relies on psychic gifts supplemented by prayer and ceremony to arrive at his conclusions. Commonly these practitioners employ hand-trembling, star-gazing, or crystal-gazing as diagnostic techniques. Here, too, no history or physical examination is included. A fee is charged for the service, although considerably less than the fee of the Singer.

For those who lack the means to afford the services of the Singer and diagnostician, symptomatic treatment is available from the lowest of Navajo practitioners, the herbalist. Symptomatic relief, however, is not equated with cure and by no means eliminates the need for a Sing when resources permit. Herbal remedies are used in times of pain, but are considered temporary relief for a still unresolved problem. Indeed the Navajo is likely to try any source of relief available to him at the time, be it herbalist, Hopi medicine man, Christian faith healer, or even PHS physician.

The PHS physician is perceived by the traditional Navajo as something on the order of (or possibly less than) the herbalist. The typical interaction between the patient and PHS clinician certainly differs from the ideal relationship between Singer and patient. The doctor spends very little time with the patient, and much of that is spent in asking questions, poking, and probing. The family is usually excluded from the treatment, either because of distance from the hospital or at the physician's request. And the physician relies on a wide range of medicinal preparations for oral, parenteral, and intravenous use.

Moreover, the symptomatic treatment offered by PHS cannot have been worthwhile, because the doctor did not charge for it. We have noted that fees are an integral part of the traditional Navajo system. Somewhat like a modern psychiatrist who believes a successful treatment may not be free, the Singer prefers charges even to members of his own family. Navajos who can afford the bills may prefer to visit a physician in private practice in an off-reservation town rather than accept free medicine.

A second built-in problem is that the physicians and the practitioners cannot communicate properly. The Navajo language, a derivative of the Athabascan tongue, is particularly difficult for unfamiliar ears. Its complexity was put to good use in World War II, when Navajos speaking in their native tongue conveyed information that no Japanese could decipher. It is said that no white man can ever hope to speak Navajo well. Personal experience leads us to doubt that anyone could use it for communication without many years of exposure.

Physicians and other health workers rapidly pick up enough phrases to obtain necessary patient behaviors—phrases such as "open your mouth," "take a deep breath," or "turn over." But it is estimated that over half the patients seen at PHS facilities on the Navajo reservation do not speak English well enough to communicate with the doctor, to give him a history, and to understand simple explanations and instructions. In view of this severe barrier, it is shocking not to find a single trained interpreter in any medical facility on the reservation. The medical staff must rely on nurses' aides and clerks to serve as makeshift interpreters as their availability permits. Thus, despite his years of professional training, the doctor's effectiveness depends on the abilities of someone who may not have completed high school to understand, translate, and interpret information and instructions.

Not surprisingly, such interpretation is inconsistent and often erroneous. The concept of a tracheostomy may be rendered by an untrained interpreter as "slitting the throat." This presentation is not likely to produce enthusiasm for the procedure. Some concepts cannot be transferred from one language to the other. If the physician, in English or through an interpreter, expresses sympathy in announcing a death, his regret may be perceived as guilt. "I am sorry to tell you that your father died" could be understood as "I am sorry to tell you I have killed your father."

Even in situations where the language barrier is less a problem, the providers of medical care still represent a system that has a history of unjust and inconsistent dealings with the Indian. The Navajo will not trust it easily.

The history of the white man's dealings with the Navajo is not a proud vista. From the early Spaniards who slaughtered and enslaved through the first American settlers who sought gold, the white man did not make a good first impression. As one commentator on the historical scene put it, "... the American frontier was not initially peopled by individuals of admirable character so that Indians began to learn Anglo ways from not too desirable white Americans" (1). Nor was the image of the white man much improved by the ravages of the cavalry and the enforced imprisonment after the Long March.

The Indians have lived through a succession of administrations from the Army, which was first charged with the responsibility of overseeing the reservation system, through the Quakers, who were tried briefly and unsuccessfully around 1928, to the Civil Service. Each new federal administration brought with it a new philosophy and a new set of policies for dealing with the so-called "Indian problem."

After a century of treatment which was consistent only for exploitation, the Navajo attitude towards the federal government and its programs resembles that of the child towards its parents. Fear, resentment, and suspicion are coupled with a desire to belong and a dependency that equates belonging to sustenance. This dependent role has been used by the government to manipulate the Indian. Whenever the latter threatens to organize to demand better treatment, the talk turns to "termination." Termination is the removal of the special status of the Indians as federal wards immune from taxation and local aggrandisement at the expense of their lands. In the 1950's, termination was the policy of government choice, with dire economic consequences for the reservations where it was implemented. At present, current thinking has put this notion into disfavor, but the Navajo know how readily and reliably things change.

This background guarantees that suspicion and lack of openness will pervade the relationship between the providers and consumers of care. It is likely that those within PHS who are most anxious to work with Navajo leadership to effect reforms will feel the most effects of the general distrust.

When PHS assumed responsibility for the health of the Indians, it inherited the general attitudes of Navajos towards their white conqueror-benefactors. But because it was new on the scene and was bringing much needed medical services, it seemed to escape the extent of ill-feeling which is directed toward the Bureau of Indian Affairs. The report, *Our Brothers' Keeper,* sums up PHS success:

> Within the context of the Indian world, the health services which are provided appear satisfactory. Not because the Indian is healthy; on the contrary his health status is as bad comparatively as his educational and economic situation. But because PHS appears so alert and businesslike, it appears an exception to the low standards generally reserved for Indians.
>
> The exception, however, is no exception. Despite its seeming autonomy, its greater professionalism, its specific achievements here and there, PHS is an integral part of the system which tends to destroy Indians and the Indian world (2).

The above statement may seem to be damning with very faint praise indeed. Yet the fact that its personnel are accepted as skilled and that the services still *appear* satisfactory to many of the consumers offers PHS some time to become a more effective and respected organization before it is too late. A totally "bad press" among the consumers would be hard to reverse given the social context of the Navajo reservation.

But PHS is hampered in its effort to gain the trust of the patient by another inherent problem, the high turnover of personnel. Since the large majority of the professional staff, particularly the physicians, are two-year men who are fulfilling a military commitment, the turnover in some Service Units approaches fifty percent per year. No sooner has a man become familiar with the system, established channels of communications, and begun to inform himself about the culture and its effects on health than he is discharged.

For the physician this short tenure can be particularly handicapping. We have already seen that Anglo medicine contains several elements which depreciate it to the traditional Navajo. The individual who provides that type of medical care must be tested. The patients are more comfortable with someone they know. The people must feel that the doctor cares about them, and they doubt whether such concern can be found in someone who leaves so quickly. The physician, for his part, needs repeated contacts with the same individuals and families to see change taking place. Only through prolonged association is he likely to derive the satisfactions of personal recognition and patient gratitude. Both the patients and the physician share a mutual longing that he be seen not as *a* doctor, but as *their* doctor. A two-year tour of duty cannot foster this rapport.

This dilemma is often defined in terms of either transitory care or no care at all. Yet other solutions are possible, particularly the use of allied health manpower. A cadre of practitioners recruited from local people could provide continuity of care at the primary level. Since they speak the language, are attuned to local customs, and plan to make their permanent homes in the area, they offer many advantages. Experience among a variety of socio-economic classes from neighborhood health centers to private practices suggests that once patients are exposed to nonphysician practitioners, they accept them readily and in many cases prefer them to physicians.

Personnel turnover creates complications beyond the difficulties with patient rapport. In smaller Service Units where two-year men constitute virtually the entire professional work force, program development may be radically influenced by the rapid turnover. A program evolved by one cohort of men can become just an echo of a memory in four or five years. Inadequate documentation of the reasons for the emphasis of a particular program and insufficient involvement of more permanent station personnel may permit newcomers to discard their predecessors' plans without proper consideration.

In part, the quick personnel changes at local levels provide the rationale for the centralized administration. But for many years the government needed little persuasion to maintain control of the reins in Washington. Policies and service commitments which could not possibly fit the individual peculiarities of each Service Unit were issued by the director of the Indian Health Service.

A vivid example of centralized program control can be found in the dental division. The dental program is based on a concept of incremental care for school children. Young children are enrolled in the program, brought up to a state of maximum dental health and then maintained each year by regular checks and necessary repair. The theory allows that, since less time is required for maintenance than for original restoration, additional groups can be added each year until eventually all children will be enrolled and followed annually. This approach was designed for maximum efficiency in the utilization of the limited dental personnel available, and is intended to be used without deviation in every establishment served by a PHS dental team.

When it was suggested that the priorities developed might not be appropriate for the needs of a particular Service Unit population, the reaction was like that of a Grand Inquisitor toward a heretic. Anger and resentment at the challenge of dogma was followed by impatient efforts at uninformative and unsubstantiated explanation, and finally by an ultimatum to "love or leave" the system. In a short time, the dentist who had asked the question found his name had reached the level of the Washington headquarters.

In an effort to centralize planning, mathematical formulae were sought which could reduce the health care needs to a series of numbers. The Indian Health Service's "Q-formula" was comprised of the loads imposed by deaths, hospitalizations, and outpatient visits of any disease entity. The Q-formula is calculated as follows (3):

$$Q = MDP + \frac{A}{N}(274) + \frac{B}{N}(91) + \frac{C}{N}(274)$$

Where

M = Health problem ratio $\dfrac{\text{(Target group rate)}}{\text{Reference Rate}}$

D = Crude target group mortality rate per 100,000

P = Years of life lost due to death

A = Numbers of inpatient days

B = Numbers of outpatient visits

C = Days of restricted activity

N = Target group population

274 = Conversion constant $\dfrac{100,000}{365}$

91 = Conversion constant $\dfrac{100,000}{365} \times \dfrac{1}{3}$

This method promised a means of comparing different diseases by looking at their relative impacts on a population. Goals and objectives could be set in terms of reducing by a certain percentage the toll of these diseases as reflected in their Q-values. The simplicity of the idea was deceptive. What functioned as a useful tool for headquarters staff was a misunderstood millstone for Service Units. Data to feed the formula were not available and too often were estimated or invented to meet headquarters' demands. Planning in mathematical abstractions had no basis in reality for the local units and could not be translated into action programs. After a few years of fruitless efforts to make the formula work, it was abandoned.

As with many aspects of government life, planning techniques have shifted with the administration in power. The strong centralized control which evolved in the early days of the Indian Health Service fell under the sway of a new philosophy of planning developed originally by the Department of Defense. Program Planning Budget System (PPBS) was intended to facilitate planning from the bottom up. Starting with programs developed by the local Service Units in terms of guidelines which relied heavily on data (or non-data) such as Q-values, plans were coalesced at the Area and headquarters levels to form a master plan. Within the system, at each level, duplications were to be recognized and avoided. Alternative methods for reaching the same objectives were framed and analyzed. But PPBS was no more successful in health than in defense. Both departments found themselves committed to a struggle they could neither understand nor handle.

With the ascendancy of the current administration, the planning cycle returned to earlier methods. Under the new system of Operational Planning, direction and initiative returned to the top. The Secretary of HEW hands down a list of objectives from which departments and divisions at each level can choose. The lower echelons are then charged with the responsibility of developing programs to implement the chosen objectives. Lying slightly outside the regular categorical organization of HEW, the Indian Health Service stands betwixt and between. PPBS was a failure and is out. Operational Planning is in but is yet to be applied in any meaningful way.

Whether the method is PPBS or Operational Planning, the effect at the Service Unit level seems to be demoralization. An officer who spent three years as a Service Unit director discussed program planning in these words:

Regarding the program plans—I have about 400 pounds of paper in my office at present called "program plans." I also recently disposed of another 100 pounds of paper which represents past attempts at program plans. Each year, and sometimes twice a year, we are asked to produce a program plan. Each time, the guide-lines, prototypes, and emphasis are changed, usually by directive from Washington. Also each year we are asked to prepare a construction document which is to request and justify needed new facilities. Each year the rules regarding the preparation of this document are changed. It is purely accidental if plans for any two years are alike even though we at the local level try to keep the plans and requests consistent with past requests. . . . We have formulated many plans and programs and yet after two years, five years, and even more the amount of visible change that we have created is very small, maybe even insignificant.

The final strike against the PHS health system on the Navajo reservation is that it is centrally funded without regard for local needs and with an emphasis on quantity rather than quality of service. Each year the Indian Health Service takes its turn before the congressional appropriations committees to seek the funds necessary to sustain and permit its growth. The plans are usually presented in terms of provision of more services to more people. Quantity of care delivered is the measure of success. Needs for more money are presented in terms of gaps in services. Each year the Indian Health Service proudly proclaims an increase of X percent in clinic visits and hospital days.

Elaborate systems featuring computer techniques are used to measure volume of service. Reports cite numbers of visits for various conditions, hospital days, hospital admissions, numbers of contacts with various health professionals, numbers of immunizations, and the like. These reporting systems also contain untapped potential to generate information about deficiencies in service and to identify needs in matters such as underutilization of appropriate laboratory tests or unnecessary repeated clinic visits by the same individual.

Unfortunately, no one asks if the services are worth rendering. The quality of the care delivered may be more important than the bald number of services dispensed. Unless the care makes an impact on the recipient, improving his life in some way, we face the prospect of what Geiger calls the revolving door of the medical care system. The same patients return again and again as treatment failures. The growing numbers, instead of indicating increasing effect, become evidence of the system's inability to provide meaningful treatment.

Once the need for an audit of the medical system is accepted, the potential for budgeting on the basis of negative data (that is, data which reflect gaps in service) can be realized. Goals can be altered to provide not necessarily more service but better service. Effectiveness and efficacy can be as important in the analysis as efficiency.

The Indian Health Service has not yet made that transition. Part of the blame must rest with the system of funding—a single lump sum justified by numerical needs. Good service is rewarded no differently than poor service. There is little opportunity for feedback. At first glance, lump sum funding seems to favor intensive preventive efforts to avoid costly hospital treatment as has been the case with several prepayment systems like the Kaiser Plan. Unfortunately, the federal programs lack any incentive to the provider. Not only is he unrewarded if by good management he reduces the load on the facility, he may also be penalized by a smaller allocation the next year on the basis of lower utilization figures.

Examples of potential misdirection within such fiscal policies come readily to mind. Beds are unnecessarily filled to maintain a high occupancy rate, thereby diluting care of the acutely ill. Increasing numbers of persons are processed through the clinics in less and less time. One can imagine that the ideal set-up for increasing service figures would be two doors with a counter in between; the patient would pause only long enough to be counted before going out the second door. This would require little space and carry a high likelihood of return visits to further swell the numbers.

Since the Indian Health Service's individual units operate on a fixed budget, pressure is exerted towards economy for most of the fiscal year. Each Service Unit operates a contract medical program and, since the demands on such a program are unpredictable, caution calls for careful spending. If, however, the end of the year finds the kitty too full, the Service Unit is encouraged to enjoy a spending spree. The Indian Health Service as a whole must not be caught with money unspent from last year's budget when it makes its new requests. Such erratic procedures do not encourage good management or consistent relationships with either one's own staff or the outside world.

In this chapter we have discussed cultural differences which devalue Anglo medical practices in the Navajo eyes, communication problems which make rapport, or even understanding, between consumers and providers hard to achieve, and historical events which cause the consumers to suspect the motivations of the providers. These problems alone could weigh down a system. But the additional burdens of high turnover, centralized planning, and funding which rewards volume rather than effectiveness of service are too much for a system which is already working uphill. The first three problems cannot be eliminated although constant awareness can lead to some amelioration of their bad effects. But the administrative machinery which produces the remaining three problems surely could be altered. The administration after all exists to serve the goals of the system, in this case the provision of excellent health care to the Indian. The danger of any bulky administrative procedure is, of course, that in time it will come to serve its own needs. The experience with the Indian Health Service is surely relevant to the new large health organizations we can expect (and desire) in the future.

REFERENCES

1. Bock, G. *Navajo area Indian Health Service program overview.* Subcommittee on Indian health of the Committee on Medical Care Administration, Indian Health

Service, Navajo Area, 1969, p. 29.
2. Cahn, E. (ed.) *Our brothers' keeper.* Washington: New Community Press, 1969, p. 55.
3. The Q-formula is discussed by Michael, J.; Spatafore, G., and Williams, E. A basic information system for health planning. *Public Health Reports,* 1968, *83,* 21-28.

Chapter III

The Indian Givers — A Study of Indian Health Personnel

What of the men and women who staff the Public Health Service's Indian health programs? Personnel are, in part, shaped by the system they work in and yet, eventually, it is they who give that system shape. Anyone who would drive a wedge into this kind of cycle must determine what sorts of persons enter the structure and how the structure affects its members.

Three groups may be distinguished in the work force of PHS on the Navajo reservation. The white careerist is the employee who has been working longest on the reservation. Since the federal government's assumption of general responsibility for the Navajo, the reservation has been beset by career administrators and providers. Those attached to the late-arriving PHS all seem to be cut out of the BIA cloth, despite the fact that some are civil servants and some are members of the Commissioned Officer Corps. This last distinction provides different career ladders, but the spirit of the civil servant and the career officer are akin.

The second identifiable group is the new breed of commissioned officer that has appeared since the passage of the Public Health Service Act in July, 1944. This is the two-year reservist who is fulfilling a short-term commitment with PHS in lieu of military service.

The third group is made up of Navajo employees who constitute the majority of the work force employed by PHS. They are members of the civil service making their careers with PHS, yet they can be considered separately from the white careerist.

In the following analysis of the three major groups, we will be generalizing without apology. Obviously some individuals do not fit their group stereotype. Nevertheless, when examining a bureaucratic structure, it is extremely useful to seek out patterns other than those inherent in the columns of the hierarchy.

22

White Careerists

The characteristics of Indian agents have been illustrated in too many western movies to leave us without certain preconceptions about the type of man who acted as liaison between the Indians and the government. The stereotype features a blackguard who dilutes the flour, sells illicit alcohol, skims off allotment checks, and gets a kickback from the trader; he may even do a little raping on the side. As is often the case, the picture is distorted both in degree and in direction. Many of the agents who served the Navajos risked their careers trying to protect the rights of their charges. The failure, time and again, of even well-motivated agents to protect the rights of the Indians shows the difficulty of struggling for reform from within the bureaucracy.

The importance and influence of white government on the reservation cannot be overemphasized. The Navajo name for the town of Shiprock is *Nataani Nez,* translated as "tall chief." The name refers to a tall agent who lived in town at the beginning of this century and to whom the Navajo needed to apply before he could farm, build, move, or resolve almost any point at issue.

The white man's power has not always been accompanied by sensitivity. The Boy Scout chapter in Window Rock, Arizona, the seat of the Navajo central government, is the Kit Carson Chapter. A street in Fort Defiance, traditional center of reservation activities, is called Kit Carson Drive. Yet it was Kit Carson who led the band of soldiers who massacred Navajo settlements, slaughtered the last warriors holding out in Canyon de Chelly, and rounded up the remnants of the Navajo tribe to begin the enforced Long March to Fort Sumner.

The BIA has been severely castigated in the report by the Citizen's Advocate Center, appropriately entitled *Our Brother's Keeper.* It is described as an agency which operates to "alienate the Indian, to perpetuate his dependency, and to thwart his every attempt at self-realization" (1). These authors see little hope of change within the BIA. Rather they describe it as a "case of terminal bureaucracy" which is organized in such a way that creativity is stifled and good motivation becomes useless. Unfortunately, PHS employees are subject to many of the same pressures as the BIA worker.

The PHS is a younger organization than the BIA and has not had as much time to become entrenched. A little more hope can be held out for PHS because it is part of HEW. (The BIA is the only agency within the Department of the Interior whose central concern is human rights.) Nonetheless, at the local Service Unit level of the Indian Health Service, we may expect the bad reputations of BIA and PHS to merge in time unless present trends among PHS employees are reversed.

The careerists at the Service Unit level, who live in the same communities as the Navajos they serve, will shape the image of PHS in Navajo circles.

The social distance between Navajo clients and PHS employees in the upper echelons of the hierarchy is increased by the fact that housing is provided and maintained for the employees by PHS in a private compound near the hospital. In Shiprock, the PHS compound is a veritable oasis because of an underground sprinkler system provided and operated by PHS grounds personnel. Walking down the tree-lined, lighted streets, the residents might find it hard to remember that telephones, power, and water are unavailable to Navajos except along the main roads of the reservation.

The life style of the careerist, who may spend many years in a given Navajo community, is important in molding his ideas and personality. Known as "Anglos," these careerists mingle little with the Navajo socially. White teenagers may have Navajo school friends, but little dating takes place between the groups. Unless the Anglo protests, he often is waited on in local businesses before a Navajo who was there ahead of him—this happens seemingly by mutual consent. In most cases the churches attended by the Anglo have white ministers, and whites and Navajos rarely socialize at church.

In many of the careerists one can sense an ambivalent attitude towards the Navajo and the reservation. On the one hand, he feels a real love of the land and, by association, its people. He may become interested in and truly admire some of the local crafts. Yet on the other hand, he despairs for the ability of the Indian ever to better himself. The careerist feels a frustration which sometimes approaches racist assumptions of inferiority or moral laxity. The Navajo may be perceived as wily, shrewd, cunning, and highly political, and also as lazy, unambitious, dependent, and unreliable. We have known careerists who have made a great mystery out of the Navajo community and taken considerable pride in their methods of intelligence. To hear such persons describe their fifth-column methods among the Navajo, one would hardly imagine that the whole effort is geared towards obtaining knowledge of the opinions and feelings of one's neighbors.

There are forces which tend to erode the careerist's ambitions. Routine is the keynote of the organization, with the promise of promotions at regular intervals and, for commissioned officers, the lure of retirement at half-pay after 20 years in service. Leading an eight-to-five life, the careerist pours his creative energy into imaginative vacation and off-hour plans. In a moment of candor, one career officer in the Commissioned Corps offered insight into this attitude: "Why should I knock myself out? What possible reason could there be? If I do my work adequately, I know that I'll be promoted regularly. It isn't as though I can expect a pay raise if I do a better job." It may be stultifying to work under these self-imposed limitations, but the career officers who make this choice are opting for security for themselves and their families. Many will be relatively young men at retirement time and then they may pursue a position in the private sector with the vigor that PHS does not demand and may not encourage.

Two-Year Men

PHS differs from other government agencies in that a substantial proportion of the professional work force is composed of two-year men. At one end of the spectrum, there are two-year men who are merely putting in time to fulfill their military obligation. But many of the two-year men are committed to utilizing their talents to the fullest potential. They infuse energy and new ideas into the system but at the same time generate restlessness and conflict with permanent personnel.

Numerically, two-year men dominate the Commissioned Officer Corps: 64 percent of the commissioned officers in the 5,545-man Corps are two-year reservists. The PHS is unique in the military in that it is composed only of officers; there are no enlisted men. Each officer has a specific skill (physician, pharmacist, dentist, social worker, nurse, engineer, or sanitarian, to name the major disciplines) and thus these men are in positions of influence and leadership.

The majority of the two-year men bring enthusiasm to the job. In part this is related to the short time they expect to be with PHS. Since they have only two years in office, they try to make the most of them, pacing themselves for a quick run rather than a prolonged trot. The two-year men come from a variety of places, bringing a variety of ideas. Fresh from training, they are filled with the most modern teaching which they are eager to apply.

The youth of the two-year people often works to their disadvantage, however. They are not readily respected either by the patients or by their fellow workers. They lack practical experience and, moreover, many of the physicians have been trained in relatively narrow fields such as internal medicine or pediatrics. They cannot respond readily to the necessity of serving as Officer of the Day in matters such as applying casts, delivering babies, or handling trauma. The doctors, in common with most medical graduates, have had little formal introduction to dealing with people or community groups, and the orientation provided by PHS is cursory indeed. The introductory material mailed to incoming officers stresses recreational opportunities in the region rather than the philosophical viewpoints of the agency.

Despite motivation and interest in the Indian's culture, the two-year man too often responds to the imperfect system with its heavy workloads by giving the patient abrupt treatment. Such an end result may seem inconsistent, but the consequence of stifled enthusiasm is often impatience and easy disillusionment.

Perhaps the degree to which the enthusiasm of the two-year man and his interest in Navajo culture can rise is best illustrated by the journal of a highly motivated and intelligent physician who had familiarized himself with Navajo ways and language before reporting for duty. He writes:

> The second patient. . . was an infant with diarrhea. I was trying to explain why, because it was viral, there was no cure in medicines, so the treatment is to replace water. Having read that the Navajo conceptualize the Life-Spirit as a wind—a wind enters with birth and departs with death—I tried to conceptualize virus as particular germ-plasm, and thus being an incomplete piece of "wind." It was clear that the idea was not getting through. Ultimately after a long time and multiple circumlocutions, I got the point across about the wind, but the basic point (about treatment) was lost.

Bearing in mind that the writer was trying to express this complex thought through the auspices of an interpreter-aide, his persistence was remarkable. The energy, imagination, and concern that motivated his rather misguided attempt are qualities that should be very valuable to PHS. As with many actions of the two-year men, however, the attempt itself proved bewildering and threatening to the patients and career personnel, and certainly frustrating to the physician.

Careerist and Two-Year Man in Conflict

The careerist and the two-year man are best described by the way they differ and come into conflict. This clash is one of the major problems in the Indian Health Service at the Service Unit level. While in many ways it is a reflection of the generation gap which confronts the whole of our society, there are some additional twists. By virtue of their professional training the two-year men often hold positions of responsibility over much older but less-educated career employees. Because of the small size of many PHS stations, two-year men have great potential influence in local policy-making.

But the two-year men do not tend to remain with PHS after their legal commitment is over. The reasons vary from financial ambitions or desire for greater professional stimulation, to feelings that nobody in the PHS is very eager to recruit them. Promotions have often gone to less able individuals who were willing to stay within the system. Within the permanent group, more-over, promotions are awarded under a lock-step system that rewards longevity rather than creativity, initiative, or hard work. This method of promotion by attrition further widens the gap between the careerist and the two-year man. The latter may occupy leadership roles at the Service Unit level but they become quickly frustrated when they are subordinated to permanent Area staff whom they do not respect as either more able or more knowledgeable.

The following table summarizes several differences in the two groups—differences which breed tensions at the Service Unit level:

Two-Year Man	Careerist
younger	older
more educated	less educated
change-oriented	favoring *status quo*
short-term outlook	long-term outlook
liberal	conservative
uncontrollable	dependent on the system
involved with Navajo culture	ambivalent about Navajo culture

The two-year man is generally younger but more educated than the careerist. For both reasons, he is more likely to be affected by the social-political movements that are sweeping the institutions of higher learning, movements which the careerist neither understands nor trusts. The careerists, moreover may harbor harsh feelings towards anyone who he feels is avoiding military service. The two-year man is recruited for a specific professional skill. As provider of a skill in short supply, his role in the delivery system is readily identifiable. The careerist is more likely to be involved in some aspect of administration, a position that is less visible and harder to justify.

Opposing philosophies of change produce the most underlying friction between the two groups. With the exuberance and energy of youth, together with the sense of urgency that a two-year stint imposes, the two-year man is anxious to initiate change as soon as he perceives a need. His sense of accomplishment is linked to concrete changes wrought by his presence. Frequently he departs the scene before the full impact and repercussions of his innovations are felt.

The careerist is understandably more cautious. He senses that he will have to live with whatever changes are evolved. Already he has adapted to a certain set of conditions. His territory is defined and his defenses are solidified against any would-be power grabbers. A change represents a potential threat. While he is aware that improvements are possible, he also knows that his own situation could be endangered if attention is drawn to uncorrected deficits or if dormant antagonisms are aroused. At the very least, change is a disruption of the equilibrium.

If change in itself is suspect, change sponsored by two-year men is poison. With half of the two-year men leaving every year, the careerist has come to view their demands for change as an annoying way of life. Those in subordinate roles must respond to these demands, but they do so with wariness and contempt. They have seen one type of activity replaced by another only to be replaced by the original. Ideas and plans seem to be perpetually rediscovered. Then too, the newcomers often approach the subject of change with an arrogance that suggests the older, more experienced man's opinion is not worth seeking. In retaliation, the careerist may resist the good ideas along with the bad.

The two-year men may find that in the local region they are treated with deference yet merely humored, while at the Area level their ideas may not be taken seriously at all. In the words of one career officer: "The 'young, angry men' we are getting tend to over-respond to upper echelon decisions; and although they are a valuable asset in pointing out our weaknesses, they are ineffectual in doing anything about it."

The careerist considers that too firm a commitment to any idea is dangerous. His advancement depends on his pleasing his superiors and this in turn depends upon keeping current with (but never anticipating) their thinking. A reputation as a trouble-maker, perhaps as a result of over-zealous pursuit of an independent idea, may curtail one's success within the system. One device to avoid being caught out of touch with current policy is simply not to make decisions. Referring all questions to one's superiors has the dual advantage of maintaining good communications and bolstering the boss's view of himself as a vital link in the process.

In contrast, the two-year man may severely threaten the system by refusing to relinquish responsibility or his commitment to an idea. Because he is not dependent on the system for prolonged sustenance and because he has had a rather extensive professional training, he may be more willing to trust his own evaluation of needed changes than that of (in the words of one young man) "a bunch of bureaucrats who have been in it so long they can't see what is happening."

Relatively few controls can be exercised over the short-termer. He can be fired (drummed out of the Corps) or transferred to the combat exposure he may have sought to avoid, but either action requires a great effort from the establishment and places it on the defensive should it be challenged. More important, the officer is there because of a need for his skills in the first place. The typical two-year man responds with cynicism or amusement to the attempt to impose a military regime at the Service Unit level. One two-year man stationed on the Navajo reservation reported an instance when his superior told him during a staff meeting that he would "strip those badges off your sleeve." Far from humiliating its object, the threat was treated as a joke, reminiscent of a line from a bad movie, and the man who uttered it lost all vestiges of respect from his staff. The challenge, therefore, becomes one of restraining men through positive direction rather than negative coercion in a setting which is successfully employing the latter tactic on the career segment.

The Indian Health Service has set out its own guidelines to describe the valued employee. A training guide for supervisors within the agency cites loyalty as the most important quality of a leader (or an employee). Loyalty takes precedence over ability, industry, or creativity. Quoting from the Indian Health Service manual, *Improving Management Practices Amid Changing Times:*

> Loyalty to the country, to Indian Health, to the organization, to
> the boss, to the men who work for you and with you—these are
> the prime requisites of *leadership* [italics in the original].

The message is clear. But one group of employees has internalized the teaching and another group decidedly has not.

The two-year man readily becomes a strong defender of the minority group. Support of civil rights is in keeping with his generation and his education. The role is all the more appealing because it is adopted in support of an unfamiliar ethnic group. He is intellectually drawn to learn the language and folkways. He can do so from a position of security, for he knows that he possesses a skill in short supply and is sure of his value to the community. Quite readily he becomes sensitive to anything which he perceives as discriminatory towards the Indian.

The white careerist does not always enjoy the same security about his role in the organization. His skills are not unique and do not demand the same level of formal education. As a more permanent resident in the community, he seeks to conform to accepted behavior patterns of nonfraternization. He is less inclined to interest himself in historical and cultural perspectives. When cultural idiosyncrasies become an impediment to increased production, his ambivalent attitude towards the Indian may lead to overt or unconscious acts of discrimination. The careerist is likely to believe that the Indian is an undeserving recipient of special prerogatives and perhaps to wonder whether his own job is in danger.

These attitudes have practical implications. For example, while we were residents, a two-year man pointed out an apparent injustice connected with employee sick leave. White employees usually had a telephone and would "call in sick" on days when they felt indisposed. The Navajo employees generally reported symptoms to their supervisors, whereupon they were obliged to visit the clinic for examination before being granted sick leave. The complaining physician claimed that the Navajos resented the procedure and that he too resented being asked to judge on the severity of a headache or cold. In this instance the sensitive antenna of the two-year man had spotted an inequity. The procedure was changed over the objections of career employees, especially in nursing, who claimed (a) this new laxity would lead to abuse of sick leave privileges among much-needed aides and (b) a good supervisor should be sure her charges receive medical attention.

The same two-year man who drew attention to the sick leave problem carried his thinking to an extreme in which he refused to participate in any off-hour activities which were designed to compensate for the understaffed nature of the hospital. For example, during several evenings many physicians volunteered their services in updating dangerously out-of-date medical charts. He refused to help, branding the effort as a stop-gap measure which prevented the PHS from eventually hiring more Navajo clerks in the record department.

Like any large and growing organization, the PHS has bred many of its own problems. Size creates gaps in communications and then attempts to wad the gaps with reams of paper. The individual loses his sense of belonging and becomes focused on his job description rather than on the job to be done. It is fascinating to compare accounts of those who manned the Indian Health Service in its first struggling years with experiences of today. Even allowing for the rosy hue which time imparts to recollections, seemingly the Indian Health Service of 1957 had much more sense of commitment, of self-reliance and of *esprit de corps* than that of 1970. The following quotation from a PHS career pharmacist expresses with more longing than literacy this sense of nostalgia for an era all too quickly past:

In the beginning the PHS offered a unique charm, for even though it is a bureaucracy, it knows its membership well. We seemed to all have a common goal, and working closely together, under very trying conditions, toward this objective. As our conditions improve our "corp de spric" [sic] and morale seem to be decaying. Might it not be wise to let the "machines" do the necessary fiscal work they are so well suited for, and leave the personnel placement and management up to the people?

It is hard to measure the lifetime of enthusiasm. Certain projects maintain vitality for generations, while others seem to wither rapidly. The plight of the Peace Corps seems also to have befallen the Indian Health Service. The participants have become more interested in what they can get from it than what they can contribute.

The Indian Health Service is aware of growing dissatisfactions. It recognized that the retention rate of two-year personnel was too low and the loss of career personnel alarmingly high. In 1968 the Navajo Area surveyed its staff to ask why people left the Indian Health Service. A look at some of the responses may yield ideas not only for PHS but for other programs that might be contemplated.

Several themes recurred in the replies. Many cited the disparity between earnings in government service and potential earnings in the private sector. Isolation, both professional and social, was frequently deplored. Opportunities for advancement seemed too slow and generally required the professional to forego his discipline and become an administrator.

But the most noteworthy frustrations were subtler. Over and over the complaint was lack of recognition. Employees felt that they were appreciated by neither the consumers nor their superiors in the hierarchy. Sometimes this complaint was couched in terms of poor morale locally and inadequate communication with the Area level. Clearly the respondents longed for the pat on the back for a job well done or even a fight well fought.

Navajo Employees

The Navajo people themselves constitute the largest part of the PHS work force on the Navajo reservation. Merely reciting numbers, however, does not show how the Navajos are primarily confined to lower grades. In only one instance has a Navajo ever acted as Service Unit director.* (Coincidentally he

*Things may be changing. Following the election of a new tribal chairman in late 1970, a Navajo was appointed as director of the BIA Navajo Area office.

is the author's successor at Shiprock and the only Navajo to have graduated from medical school.) In the Shiprock Area only four of the 18 registered nurses were Navajos and there were no Navajos among the sanitarians, dentists, or pharmacists. On the other hand all the LPN's, nurses' aides and janitors were Navajo.

Indian people working in their own communities form the backbone of the organization and provide the potential for its ultimate success. Ironically these are the persons most dependent on the system and least likely to make any efforts to change it. Too often they mutely accept policies inflicted by others, bending with prevailing trends but unconfident that they represent a permanent improvement.

In some ways the Navajo employee resembles the careerist. A majority of educated Navajos were raised in BIA schools, which espoused the values of the dominant culture's bureaucracy. White careerists like to point to incidents which show that Navajo hospital employees are indifferent to the suffering of Navajo patients. But this is a judgment which is usually made out of context without considering either cultural norms or clan relationships. (A Navajo will often behave differently towards a member of his own clan.)

The very quality which makes the Navajo the hope of the health care system also makes him vulnerable. He is tied to the reservation. By whatever bonds a man is linked to his home, the Navajo usually wants to remain on the reservation. He has resisted massive deportation efforts by the cavalry and later resisted the BIA's relocation programs. But jobs on the reservation are scarce. Despite efforts to attract private industry, the primary employers remain the government (in the shape of BIA, PHS, and lately OEO) and the Navajo Tribe itself, through its tribal enterprises.

With the demand for jobs exceeding the supply, the Navajo is loath to rock the boat. Not infrequently local tribal politicians try to restrain opposing opinions by bringing pressure through job supervisors. This pressure can be effective because the supervisor's success in turn depends on an ability to gain cooperation of the local politicos.

The political pressure placed on Navajo employees of the federal government was dramatically illustrated to us early in our Shiprock experience. Because of some community discontent with the elected president of the Shiprock Chapter, a petition was circulated among his constituents asking for an investigation of his administration. A few employees of PHS signed the document. Very shortly the Chapter president himself was in the office of the Service Unit director demanding that he control his employees and make support of the tribal leadership a condition of employment. From the tone of the request, we gathered that it was by no means unusual and that the president expected cooperation as a matter of course.

The careerists can afford to encourage Navajo employment at the lower levels of the occupational ladder but they reject outright any thoughts of putting them in managerial positions in competition with whites. Anglos with very little formal education and a wealth of on-the-job experience are quick to reject Navajos as insufficiently educated for jobs like their own. Thus, we find Navajos trained as aides—it is amazing how many different kinds of aides we can create.

The absurdity of excluding Navajo employees from the mainstream of promotion and reward becomes more apparent when we realize that these are the only employees who can truly communicate with the patients. From their lowly position as aides, Navajo employees are asked to interpret for the physicians but, as we will discuss later, are not trained for this important function

We have described three groups of workers each with something important to contribute to the PHS system, each dissatisfied with the organization and his opportunity for power within it, and each feeling rather hopeless to overcome his problems. No matter how worthwhile the goals of the Washington office, a work force like this will have difficulty uniting to put them into effect.

REFERENCE

1. Cahn, E. (ed.) *Our brother's keeper.* New Community Press: Washington, 1969, p. 141.

Chapter IV
"Indian Involvement and Participation"

The Indian Health Service is pledged to work towards its goals "using Indian involvement and participation to the fullest possible extent" (1). In most practical cases, "possible extent" is defined by the PHS employees at the local level, aided and abetted by local tribal politicians.

Indian governments, as they exist today, are a testimony to the BIA's diligent efforts to organize tribal bodies with whom they might conveniently deal. The Indian Reorganization Act, passed by Congress in 1934, provided for representative governments for each tribe. All tribes were to decide by plebiscite whether they were willing to accept the suggested form of self-government. In 1934 the Navajo narrowly voted down the implementation of the act for their reservation. As an early example of the application of the principle of Indian self-determination, the BIA proceeded to deal with the newly created Navajo Council as if it had received the endorsement of the tribe (2). The most important concern of the BIA at the time was its own need to deal with some representative Navajo body on the matter of rights to newly discovered oil on the reservation.

The Navajo system is a microcosm of the American representational system. Each locality, known as a Chapter, elects representatives to the Navajo Tribal Council. This body is the central governing organ. It meets in the Navajo capital, Window Rock, which not coincidentally is also the seat of the central BIA and PHS administrative machinery for the Navajo Area. The entire tribe votes for a tribal chairman and vice-chairman, who preside over the duly elected tribal council. Elections are held every four years and generate great interest and excitement.

Historically the tribal council's function was to approve or disapprove measures initiated by the United States government and to act as an advisor to the Indian agencies. The council was not originally expected to draft legislation. Since World War II, however, it has become a more powerful legislative body and has been permitted to dispose of large sums of federal

34

funds which have been channelled through the tribal government.

The local Chapters are also headed by elected officials. The political power structure of a community such as Shiprock is composed of the president and vice-president of the local Shiprock Chapter and the Chapter's representative to the tribal council. Chapter meetings are held regularly and are open to all Navajos in the region. They are rather like town meetings and tend to be lengthy deliberations in keeping with the Navajo custom of resolving issues by achieving unanimity. Indeed all adults may speak at the meetings, but the unanimity is illusory. The local officials are adept at wielding that foreign tool, parliamentary procedure. Not uncommonly votes are taken after dissidents from the "party line" have left the room.

We have noticed that many Navajos seem to distrust their government. The attitude is one of hopelessness laced with contempt. Perhaps Navajos have observed too many tribal governments working intimately with the federal agencies. Of course, "rugged individualism" is an American tradition. In many sections of the United States citizens suspect that government does not conform to their needs and wishes. The complaint is most common in rural, isolated parts of the country, and perhaps with some justification. But the Navajo probably have much clearer grounds for rejecting their mini-American government—their government within a government.

The Navajo government was not a Navajo idea. Early observers of uncontaminated Navajo culture point out that the Navajos were never organized centrally and, even in smaller communities, had divided leadership. Loyalties were first towards the extended families and then towards the clans (larger groups of related families). Headmen were recognized in given districts for their superior wisdom or skills but their legal powers were limited. Certainly, running for office, with all the necessary currying of favor and self-advertisement, seems foreign to all descriptions of Navajo culture. Leadership is recognized and accepted by the community, but modesty would forbid openly seeking it.

In creating governmental bodies on the Navajo reservation for its own convenience, the Indian Service unwittingly acted for the convenience of the men who became the Navajo politicians but were not necessarily the Navajo leaders. The following passage from the anthropological classic of Kluckhorn and Leighton is still applicable:

Navajos understand responsibility to relatives and even to a local group, but they are only commencing to grasp the need for thinking in tribal terms. Further, they have no notion of representative government. They are accustomed to deciding all issues by face-to-face meetings of all the individuals involved, including, most decidedly, the women. The native way of deciding an issue is to discuss it until there is unanimity of opinion or until the opposition feels it no longer worthwhile to urge its point of view. Moreover because they are not familiar with the representative principle, the People by no means always send to Council the men who really count in local affairs. This fact, and the comparatively small number of women in responsible positions, tend to make Council meetings more a sounding board for ambitious politicians than a true expression of tribal sentiment (3).

Red Power has not been accepted on the Navajo reservation as a meaningful tactic. Pan-Indian movements in general have not appealed to the Navajo, and the tribe does not belong to the National Congress of American Indians. On other, smaller reservations, Indians have become aware of the effectiveness of activist groups in confronting the system. The Navajo does not now favor this kind of activity. Ironically, just as the Navajo government was originally organized by Anglos, Anglo lawyers and VISTA volunteers seem to be organizing much of the opposition. The majority of Navajos do not seem to be political in the usual sense of the word, and certainly geographic and cultural factors militate against a reservation-wide group of social activists.

Yet there are slogans and issues which the politician can use to muster his forces. The Navajo reservation is a conservative region, in the same sense that many rural, isolated areas of Anglo society are conservative. Change is distrusted and feared. The elected officials, especially at election time, are given to listing all their valuable contacts with United States and state senators, all their trips to Washington to protect a program or a boundary line, and their various strategies against potential Congressional incursions over Navajo land and resources. Little evidence suggests that the tribal politicans have often been able to impose their wishes over those of Congress, but Navajo voters find it reassuring to know that their leaders have the ear of representatives of Anglo government.

Oddly enough for an oppressed people, the Navajo respond very strongly to patriotic motivations; flag-waving is as common as at a Fourth of July parade. Navajos have a record of distinguished military service. During World War II, Navajos made a remarkable contribution by broadcasting messages in their native tongue —a code the Japanese were never able to decipher. Thirty-six hundred Navajos served in World War II (800 of them volunteers), while an additional 15,000 Navajos worked at defense-related jobs. As with other groups whose opportunities have been limited, the military has provided an escape route and a chance for success. Currently, over 1,000 Navajos are serving in Vietnam.

Present-day Navajo leaders have also assimilated many of the views of their BIA teachers. Political conservatism, coupled with patriotic fervor, has been part of their education. Unfortunately, this unquestioning acceptance of the chauvinistic line may be continuing in the younger generation. In 1970, Shiprock High School graduated a class of over 100; all but four were Navajo. Yet on the request of the graduating class itself, the guest speaker was an Anglo who addressed the group on their chosen topic, "Patriotism." It was a standard speech, though the reference to "our founding fathers" was inappropriate to the group. His remarks belittling dissenters received heavy applause.

This Navajo patriotism produces a rather unusual relationship between the Navajos and those whites who would urge them to alter the *status quo.* Some PHS two-year men, who express a genuine belief that the Navajo should control their own affairs, also voice sincere objections to the Vietnamese War. Often these men display a casual approach to the required wearing of a military uniform. But the majority of the Navajo support the Vietnamese War and believe that a military uniform should be worn carefully and correctly. On these issues they are at one with the careerists in the organization. Even in the face of PHS budget restrictions, Navajos do not respond with protest to the fact that the Vietnam War is drawing money away from domestic programs such as health. It is very possible that the groups attempting to mobilize the Navajos as a political force would achieve better success were it not for their "hippie" image and outspokenly liberal viewpoint.

The goals of PHS are theoretically committed to "Indian involvement and participation to the fullest possible extent." But no single group represents the Navajo health consumer any more than a single group represents the general American patient. Although one might first look to the Navajo elected officials, they, like American elected officials, are probably not typical in their experiences as patients. And, after settling on the appropriate consumers, at what point are they to be injected into the hierarchy? The Shiprock Navajo are served by a local medical system which is part of the Navajo Area, which in turn is part of the larger unified system which serves all Indians and Alaskan Natives.

The Indian Health Service's answer to the problem of gaining Indian involvement in the individual Service Units has come in the form of a new group of health workers known as Community Health Representatives (CHR).

These individuals are hired by the tribal governments and are paid by the tribe through a PHS grant which supports the program. The CHR is intended to serve as a liaison between the communities and the health system.

CHR's are selected directly by the tribes and do not have to conform to any rigid qualifications. In fact, they range from men and women with almost no education to college graduates, with a majority of high school graduates. At the outset of the program the tribe appoints a CHR coordinator who acts as the titular head at each Service Unit, supervising the individual CHR's and dealing directly with Chapter officials and medical personnel. An overall coordinator is also appointed for the entire Area.

The CHR's receive four weeks of intensive training at the Indian Health Service Training Center in Tucson, Arizona. The course focuses on communication skills, socio-cultural concepts, concepts of health and disease, and technical skills suggested by the particular tribes. The latter could include such instruction as principles of first aid, home nursing, environmental health or defensive driving. The CHR's then return to their home base region where they receive an additional two to six weeks of training from local officials and health professionals so that they become aware of the range of health and health-related services in their communities.

Then the CHR's begin to function in the community. Since July, 1969, when the first field units went into operation, the CHR's have been forging out a practical definition of their role while PHS employees have been eagerly watching on the sidelines. The CHR function has been interpreted in various ways, ranging from performance of specific aide-like offices for health professionals, to assumption of a liaison position between the Indian community and all health and social resources, to the very comprehensive role of community developer in the health field. These roles are not mutually exclusive—certainly in Shiprock we found the CHR's performing in all of these capacities at some time.

The CHR program calls for independence of the CHR from health personnel. According to the Indian Health Service's own statement in a publication called *Community Health Representative: A Changing Philosophy of Indian Involvement:*

The staffs of the Indian Health Service medical facilities have been asked to walk a tightrope in their relations with this program. They have been asked to cooperate with the program but not to control the program. In some Service Units, the health service interactions with the program have resulted in over-control of the program by the health service, while in other communities the health service efforts to avoid controlling the program have resulted in ignoring the program (4).

The CHR's are probably in more danger of being controlled by political groups than by the health establishment. They report directly to the tribe but represent a potential power bloc of articulate spokesmen with ears to the community. Apparently in some tribes—but not so far in the Navajo tribe—the CHR's quickly became a well-accepted community force and threatened political leaders to the extent that they sought either to dominate the CHR's or to isolate them.

After a year of experience with the CHR program, a study was undertaken to determine the attitudes and expectations which both Indian Health Service personnel and Indians themselves held towards the new project. Though the two groups surveyed generally agreed on the objectives of the CHR program, each developed a different set of priorities. The Indian people perceived a primary need for the CHR's to help the Indian Health Service understand the culture and wishes of the tribe; the health professionals put much more importance on the need to help the Indians understand PHS programs and philosophy. The Indians expected that the program would have a direct effect on morbidity and mortality, while the health personnel expected an increase in the ability of Indian communities to identify and solve their own health problems. The most common concern among the professionals was the possibility that the program would produce unsupervised health care or would disseminate inaccurate health information. The Indian respondents, with understandable wariness, were more concerned that the CHR program might be used as an excuse for reducing existing PHS services.

Amid such conflicting aims and expectations, the CHR's themselves sometimes had difficulty perceiving their roles. Especially at the outset, some CHR's seemed more comfortable with a concrete service function, such as transporting patients to clinics. PHS employees at the Service Unit level were only too pleased to accept any additional manpower offered. But the CHR groups took their complex positions seriously and, in Shiprock at least, seemed interested in the health education aspects of their jobs. There the CHR's showed interest in administering a Navajo language questionnaire at the home level to assess the feeling of consumers towards the health services provided to them. This study, which was enormously useful to the hospital administration, gave the CHR's a concrete task at a time of difficulty in role establishment as well as an instrument to begin making judgments about health care. The CHR's asked particularly that a question be added to the study about desired subjects for health education.

In the whole Navajo area the CHR's embraced their ill-defined status with enthusiasm and idealism. These are the words of Thomas Todacheeney, the coordinator of the program for the Navajo Tribe, in his introduction to the CHR Operations Manual:

> I realize that our new organization will not be fully accepted overnight by certain Indian Health Service personnel and other agency staff as well as some of the Navajo families. However, you must not be discouraged by the attitudes or unkind remarks made by narrow-minded individuals. A famous person once said "the best weapon to use in some situations is to be extra kind and respectful to those that have less respect for you."

> I know all of you are well qualified in working with your own people and have received wonderful training to undertake this important assignment given by Navajo families, who would like to have better health in the future, providing that proper guidance and assistance are rendered by all the Community Health Representative staff. The majority of the Tribal Council members and Indian Health Service staff support the new program and its personnel. Therefore, put your past experience and fine training to good use. In doing so, think seriously about the late President Kennedy's remark, "Ask not what your country can do for you, but ask what you can do for your country" (5).

What the CHR can do for his country, that is, his Navajo country, is not yet clear. But the concept is an interesting one, and the Indian Health Service should be commended for financing the experiment.

The CHR's may eventually make an even greater contribution than the PHS planners ever envisaged. One of the great advantages of the OEO program on the Navajo reservation is that it was an excellent training ground for administrators—it offered Indians an education in working within and around the system. (The re-education programs of the BIA are heavily geared towards blue collar skills such as welding or hairdressing; there is no market for welders and hairdressers on the reservation, but administrators, teachers, secretaries and bookkeepers are badly needed.) Even in one year, an observer can notice that the CHR program is similarly educating its staff in health administration. CHR's as a group, or even more feasibly as individuals, might become leaders of a more demanding group of consumers. And a demanding group of consumers with some knowledge about effective methods of expressing their demands is a prerequisite for "Indian involvement and participation to the fullest possible extent."

A different approach to encouraging Indian involvement in health programs is the Indian board of directors. The Indian Health Service, on a national level, has given some recognition to this idea.

Dr. Taylor McKenzie, a Navajo and the present Service Unit director at Shiprock, has been outspoken in his belief that Navajo boards of directors should control their institutions. Speaking at an education conference, Dr. McKenzie drew an analogy about the medical situation which bears quoting in full:

I have advocated now, for some time, the local control of hospitals on the Navajo reservations on the grounds that:

1. The people would identify more with their respective hospital and its problems and would be willing to help solve mutual problems out of mutual concern.

2. There are certain decisions about medical and health services relating to and affecting Navajos that only Navajos can make. These certain decisions, if made unilaterally by the hospital and its administrative staff, would only engender resentment and suspicions: while on the other hand these difficult decisions would be more readily acceptable to the general population if they were made by a board of local Navajos.

3. Many helpful suggestions, instructions, and requests coming from the local community would tend to improve the general quality of the medical and health services, and no one need suggest that this input by the people in concert would not be practical or useful, for I have seen Navajos in groups at local community levels produce some startling and extremely intelligent decisions.

4. There would be established a mutual working understanding between the hospital and the community which it proposes to serve, for I envision the direct interchange, not only as a useful working institution, but also as an enlightening educational process for both parties concerned. And who would deny, leastwise the hospital and the medical personnel that there is a need to educate one another? (6).

Dr. McKenzie's ideal is far from realized. Officially the Indian Health Service supports the notion of advisory boards for the various Areas. The decision was passed down from Washington headquarters and the Navajo Area office was quick to comply. The advisory boards are constituted a little differently in different Areas. In the Navajo Area, the board is composed of five members of the Navajo Tribal Council (appointed by the chairman of the tribe) and the eight coordinators of the Community Health Representative Program. The CHR coordinators, as noted above, are also political appointments of the tribal council. They are, thus, insiders on two counts: they are part of the tribal political structure and part of the health system.

Then too, the members of the board represent all geographic regions of the vast Navajo Area. The board is necessarily much more a formal than a working group, since each Service Unit's problems and needs are particular. With the use of this instrument, an Area director can impose a central philosophy on the Service Units and label it a "response to the will of the people."

As yet the Service Units have not received the go-ahead to set up their own health boards. At this level, community representation could be more useful and meaningful. Preliminary dealings with consumers at the Service Unit level, however, suggest many obstacles that local consumer boards would face.

Consumers may be involved in a health system for three distinct purposes. They may be present as sources and disseminators of information. If the purpose is to keep the medical system in touch with its constituency, then the consumers should represent as broad a base as possible. The average patient provides more useful feedback than the politican whose experiences could not be typical.

On the other hand, the consumers may also be acting as policymakers. If a consumer body within a federalized system is to have any impact on policy, it must be a politically effective group which can, if necessary, have regulations changed or set aside. In this case, representatives of the local power structure would be an invaluable asset.

A third, more cynical use of consumer boards is as a token response to public pressure for involvement. Even a semblance of community consultation goes far towards creating the impression that the opinions of the patients matter. The creation of formal boards such as the Navajo Area Advisory Board serves this function admirably: the people are dignified by the ritual of approving agency action and more vigorous efforts at consumer participation are forestalled. In such instances, the consumer board acts as pacifier of the people.

Our assumption is that consumer participation in health planning is highly desirable. Mayor John Lindsay of New York City put the position well in describing the relationship between the consumer and the various government programs in New York:

> Poor planning then is a danger when government and citizens lose touch with each other. But it is not the only drawback of this top-down method of decision making. We must understand that Americans, across all lines of race, background, class and age have paid a high price for distant, impersonal power. That price is the pervasive deepening sense that citizens and government are no longer pursuing common ends. . . . I believe rather that those responsible for government—local, state and federal officials—must begin to open the way for participation and toward growing autonomy for citizens as citizens, in their own communities. Further, I believe that we will gain from this new kind of planning not simply more participation, but better planning, better delivery of services, and even the beginnings of a restored faith of the people in their government (7).

Unfortunately, there is not easy access to the opinions of the consumers of the Indian Health Service's programs. The local tribal politicians control the direct path of PHS personnel to the public. The politician does not desire an open and vigorous discussion of the flaws in the health system. Such a dialogue might disrupt his relationships with government agencies and also risk some of his own importance as the figure who influences Washington to provide the existing services. When improvements are made—usually in terms of additional facilities or budgetary increases—they are made under the auspices of tribal leaders.

We discovered this the hard way. From the moment of assuming office, we felt that the people should be taken into confidence on the "facts" of medical system. They should know the limitations of staff and budget, the incidence of disease in the region, and the utilization patterns of the hospital. We planned this not in the spirit of excusing poor performance but as an effort at opening up real communications and allowing the people to have a part in choosing priorities. Moreover, we felt that precise knowledge on the part of the consumers might relieve bitterness over inadequacies in service. The energies spent complaining over grievances could be better spent applying

From the October, 1970, edition of *Dine Baa-Hani*, a Navajo newspaper published for the Navajo nation. By permission of the publishers.

political pressure for improvements.

The elected officials in Shiprock were distinctly cool to the proposal that the Service Unit director should present the unvarnished facts of the medical system to the consumers at a Chapter meeting. Some of the smaller Chapters did ask him to speak at regular meetings, but the first interest in Shiprock was expressed by a group of young men who were the town's closest equivalent to social activists. This group asked the Service Unit director to speak to them about the health situation at one of their meetings.

The day after the talk some very irate Chapter officials complained that the author had "gone over the head of the Chapter" and bypassed the proper authorities, thereby lending legitimacy to a fringe group. The activist group had planned to sponsor a public meeting to air the health issue; the Chapter officials preempted the gathering. They would have preferred not to raise the matter but since it came up, they felt it essential to retain control. When the meeting took place, its effect was further dissipated by the presence of Navajo Area officials, invited by Chapter leaders, so that the procedure took on a formal tone. It was also a reminder to the Service Unit personnel that the muscle in the PHS organization is higher up the ladder.

Officials resent any attempt to gather information which is not filtered through them. But, as said before, officials are not the consumers to best keep the Service in touch with the people. On the other hand, the power structure contains exactly the consumers needed to bring about change in policy, and that is not a role the politicos wish to assume.

Obviously, an effectively composed board of directors is not going to spring up easily in this infertile soil. Perhaps because of the very difficulty in envisaging the creation of such boards, they have been invested with a magical quality. But many problems would remain in conceptualizing the function of a board in a centralized system. What powers would be invested in the board to dictate policy, control finances, or hire personnel? If the local board is permitted real powers, how will the federal government maintain standards? Can there be real control without control of the purse strings? Eventually the question of the appropriate role of the lay board of directors in the medical system must be raised.

Throughout the medical care systems of this country, the consumer is not always utilized as a consumer. Ideally his responsibility should be to define problems and the administration should pose technical solutions. Then the board would have the right to challenge the technicians as to whether their solutions really are meeting the problems and demand accountability. This kind of give and take could only exist in an atmosphere of mutual confidence between the consumers and the providers. In the Indian Health Service the history is less happy. In the past the providers have patronized and underestimated the consumers, and in the past the consumers have deeply mistrusted the providers. Unless the cast of characters changes dramatically, the mere appointing of local boards would not solve the problems, but add another ingredient to complicate the system.

REFERENCES

1. Program report and plan, Indian Health Service, fiscal years 1971-1975. Mimeo from IHS Headquarters, 1970 (see Introduction, p. 2).
2. Kluckhohn, C. & Leighton, D. *The Navajo*. (Rev. ed.) New York: 1962, p. 159.
3. *Ibid.* 160-161.
4. Rund, N. H., Myhre, R. D., & Fuchs, M. *Community health representative; A changing philosophy of Indian involvement.* Office of Program Development, Indian Health Service, 1970, p. 10.
5. Tribal community health representative program—plan of operation. Public Services Division, Navajo Tribe, May, 1969.
6. McKenzie, T., from a speech at the 12th annual Conference on Navajo Education, Shiprock Civic Center, April 17, 1970. Quoted in the *Navajo Times,* April 23, 1970.
7. Lindsay, J. V. *The city.* New York: W. W. Norton & Co., 1969, pp. 122-123.

Chapter V

Coffee Breaks, Shots and an Open Heart:
Some Patients' Opinions

Navajo patients make their own judgments about white man's medicine and the form in which they receive it. We have collected some reactions of patients within the Shiprock Service Unit. Translated from Navajo, the words constitute an eloquent indictment of the PHS system.

> *"Seventy miles to PHS is too far—especially when you are on foot and sick."* (Female, age 27)

> *"I waited too long for the doctor—waiting in line, lobby, hallway, in office, and for medicine. Just waiting all the way."* (Female, age 50)

> *"Us elders, we have to pay $15 to get to Shiprock from here. Mostly we have to sit in the back of a truck."* (Male, age 81)

These quotations are drawn from a study of the feelings and opinions of the Navajo consumer. The research was very simple in design; it was planned as an initial attempt at establishing communications. A questionnaire* was translated into Navajo and administered at the hogan level by the Community Health Representatives. Occupying an intermediary position between the people and the health system, the CHR's were logical choices to conduct the interviews. Each CHR completed as many questionnaires as possible in the course of his daily activities during a six-month period. The interviews were held in homes or sometimes in a central gathering spot such as a trading post. Because we were interested in thoughtful and uninfluenced individual opinion, no interviews were conducted during or following large gatherings such as Chapter meetings.

---

* See Appendix A for a copy of the questionnaire.

The CHR's were instructed in interview technique and asked to record replies verbatim whenever possible. Two hundred seventy-one questionnaires were completed by an almost equal number of male and female respondents. The sample was not randomly selected, though it was drawn from all the Service Units covered by the CHR's. Our effort was not to be scientific but to seek some immediate feedback on how patients react to the medical system, especially in rural areas.

The respondents were asked what they considered the most important health problems in their community. Eighteen percent of the 429 answers cited alcoholism as a major health problem. After alcohol, the tendency was to name specific diseases—13 percent for the common cold, eight percent for diarrhea, five percent for flu, and 14 percent for other diagnoses. Communicable diseases in general, ranging from flu and cold through ear and eye infections, impetigo and tuberculosis, received 35 percent of the responses.

After naming health problems, the participants were asked, "What can we do about them?" Out of 230 suggestions, 22 percent were in favor of generally increased medical service, six percent specified enlargement or construction of a facility, and six percent wanted a new specific service. A surprising 24 percent suggested more emphasis on health education. Women and younger persons seemed to favor this solution. Environmental approaches were seldom emphasized. The environmental solution mentioned most often was improvement of water supply, occurring in five percent of the replies.

Comparing the perceptions of the people interviewed with the actual causes of death and hospitalization on the reservation, we find that the patients had sized up the problems quite accurately. The leading cause of mortality is accidents (24 percent of the deaths in 1968)—many are related to alcohol. Senility and ill-defined conditions is the next cause of mortality (12 percent), followed by respiratory disease (11 percent), diseases of the digestive system (9.8 percent), diseases of the circulatory system (9.6 percent), and infections and parasitic diseases (9.2 percent). Admissions to Shiprock hospital reflect this trend, with accidents accounting for 13 percent, respiratory diseases 11 percent, and digestive system diseases eight percent of admissions. In the outpatient clinic 18 percent of the visits were for respiratory diseases, nine percent for disease of the nervous system and sense organs (including eye and ear), seven percent for infections and parasitic diseases, and six percent for diseases of the digestive tract. For a variety of reasons, no good statistics exist on levels of alcoholism, but no observer doubts that the rate is alarmingly high. Similarly, the pediatrician estimates that diarrhea and impetigo are very common pediatric problems.

Despite a lack of familiarity with medical jargon, the patients had a good general idea of the problems common to the area. They recognized the prevalence of respiratory problems, infectious diseases, and difficulties which called for eye and ear specialists. And certainly the patients cited alcohol as a grave health problem. As one elderly man put it, rather belligerently: "Wine no good for anybody—young generation should be taught drinking is *bad. White man make wine*—they should be responsible."

Unfortunately, the respondents did not carry their thinking a step further on the alcohol problem; very few labeled automobile accidents as a major health problem. Perhaps a clue lies here for the direction of future health education efforts.

When people were asked about problems or difficulties they might have encountered in getting help at the Shiprock hospital or clinics, a Pandora's box was opened. Out of 393 answers to this question, 49 percent focused angrily on inordinate waiting for service. Unexpectedly, eight percent complained that records were continuously lost or confused. Seven percent mentioned a shortage of physicians and another seven percent poor language interpretation. One of these latter respondents put the problem in a new perspective by saying, "Full-time Navajo interpreter is needed for those who don't speak foreign language." In this case, the foreign language he alludes to is English! Five percent deplored uncourteous and disrespectful attitudes which they perceived in hospital staff. Six percent felt a specific dissatisfaction with the nature of services rendered—among those were persons who wanted a shot and did not receive it.

Finally the participants were asked what other services they would like to have which are not presently available in the Shiprock Service Unit. Eighteen percent of the 333 replies called for a bigger hospital. Forty-nine percent wanted more staff; this figure breaks down into 14 percent asking for a general increase in personnel, 14 percent wanting eye specialists, 12 percent specialists in general, and nine percent calling for dental specialists. Six percent felt a need for an old age facility on the reservation.

While reviewing the questionnaires, the coders were struck by a theme running throughout the responses. This was the complaint that the patient had not received "shots" at Shiprock hospital. Thirty-three of the 271 completed questionnaires (12 percent) expressed this anger at some point in the interview.

Since the questions were asked in Navajo by persons not directly identified with the delivery of care, the replies were frank and vigorous. The patients' deep resentment over what they considered impolite or unkind behavior on the part of hospital personnel is clearly expressed:

> *"Well, while being hospitalized I feel like I am hated by all the nurses because I call for help every time I need assistance. I wish there were nurses who can be more friendly."*

> *"We need a good doctor just like they have in town because lots of these doctors at Shiprock were not very good and not kind to the Indian people especially the older people."*

> *"We like doctors and nurses be enthusiasm in their patients and know how to encourage them and not discourage the patient and make them feel sicker."*

Not only white employees came in for censure. Indeed the bitterness is even greater against Navajo employees, who are often met in their capacity as interpreters:

> *"Nurses aide did not interpret what my problem really was to the doctor. She was mean to me."*

> *"Navajo women employees in O.B. too rough with the new mother."*

> *"Usually some Navajo employees do not use their manners or respect."*

> *"Interpreter do not cooperate with me. One time one of the nurses told me wash my own son."*

It was eye-opening for the hospital staff to realize the extent to which they were silently condemned by an apparently stoical group. As in other studies, this data shows more anger over the manner of care than the ability or inability to cure.

The hospital staff, of course, were aware that the patients are forced to wait long hours before receiving attention. The lines are highly visible and demoralize workers.* It was not startling to find 49 percent of the respondents complaining of the situation. But the hostility in the phrasing of the

---

* Guilt among physicians over excessive patient waiting is illustrated by our observation that the patients were much more likely to get the shot they wanted with less clinical reason in the late afternoon than in the early morning.

replies was unsettling. Misconceptions about the reasons for the delays were common:

> *"When you go to Shiprock clinic you have to wait half a day before they get to you or if any white people come in they take them first. . . They should have more on duty on the floor and slow down on coffee break."*

> *"Before they wait on patients they have to have coffee break and what-not."*

> *"Waiting too long because doctors are just taking their sweet old time and talking away with each other."*

> *"Navajo have agreed to have a good hospital and was promised it but the people are using it for training the doctor. Just yesterday I took my baby there and had to wait too long so we just decide to take him to Farmington hospital."*

A clear picture is developing. In the opinion of many patients, the doctors waste their time in idle chatter and coffee breaks while sick people wait. Also, the doctors are in training and not sufficiently skilled to function at high speed. Finally the doctors, however unskilled and lazy, would never ask a white person to wait so long. Add to this the rather widespread belief that names on records are commonly lost, and we have enough ingredients to produce a dissatisified patient before he ever begins treatment. At best the patients are in an angry and unconfident mood; at worst they endanger themselves by leaving. As one woman said: "I get prescription medicine when I go there for it. Sometimes they never get around to me so I just leave without the medicine."

Once medical personnel recognize the feelings of the patients about the long waiting, efforts may be made to minimize it, or at least remove the misunderstandings surrounding the delay. The record room procedure can be scrutinized with emphasis on the manner in which the patients are asked to wait. The families of physicians can come by appointment either very early or very late, or else they can be summoned by telephone at convenient times. Justifiably, patients are indignant to see a PHS wife march into the hospital and directly into the doctor's office. Medical diplomas might be displayed conspicuously to relieve anxieties that the doctors are only students. And physicians could be careful to hold their necessary conferences in private rooms instead of in the corridors in view of waiting patients

Small steps could be taken to give some comfort to the waiting area. Many of the respondents mentioned that waiting was an endurance test without food. The risk of going to a restaurant was a risk of losing one's turn in line. Many of the patients echoed the sentiments of the man who said, "We need a sandwich machine because we wait all day and get starved." Others mentioned that fresh coffee (a favorite Navajo beverage) would be welcome. Some even called for entertainment. Such suggestions are not as frivolous as they first sound. If lengthy waits are a necessary evil of the system, all possible steps should be taken for the comfort and convenience of the patients and their families during their enforced stay. "Entertainment" can provide health education, but would be justified as an end in itself.

Even more than the delay itself, some people resented the fact that the very sick wait along with the less ill. Numerous suggestions were made that those with fevers should be seen first. The Shiprock hospital staff did discuss the possibility of a triage officer screening the patients to ensure that those in great distress see a physician immediately. Such a triage system would have eliminated a regrettable incident which occurred during the height of the flu epidemic last winter. The clinic was heavily overcrowded and an announcement was made in English and in Navajo that those with routine problems might help very much by postponing their visit for a few days. Among those who left was a man who had sustained a concussion from a riding accident. The next day he suffered seizures and had to be returned to the hospital.

The patients studied expressed their complaints clearly. These complaints focused on problems in the matter of care. But the same people made suggestions which did not address themselves to their major complaints. Forty-nine percent of the suggestions were for more staff, and 18 percent for a bigger hospital. Yet one could enlarge staff and hospital without reducing the strained relationships between patient and personnel, assisting in communication, eliminating the problems of travelling to the hospital, or even appreciably reducing the waiting time. A very few respondents did call for increased or improved interpreters or more use of Navajo traditional medicine, but the majority complained of a system which was not meeting their needs and then asked for more of the same. This observation in no way belittles the understanding of Navajo patients—it merely re-emphasizes that technical solutions are not the appropriate task of the medical consumer.

After a two-year physician spends a short time on the Navajo reservation, he becomes aware of the phenomenon of the shot-seeking patient. Seemingly a shot is considered the truly potent force in white man's medicine and is sought for a wide range of ailments. A Navajo-speaking lady who had occasion to sit in the waiting room one day told us she overheard much speculation about which doctors might be more likely to give shots. If antibiotic injections are withheld for common colds or viral flu, the resentment is keen:

"You have to be almost dying before you can get a shot."

"You don't really get the treatment you want especially for a cold—no shots, just the cough syrup—sometimes won't help at all."

We even find some patients relegating everything but shots into the realm of non-treatment:

"Hospital should give treatment to patient rather than just check them. Like shots rather than pills."

The doctors at the PHS hospital are very aware that the patients sometimes take their eagerness for a shot into the neighboring towns where they usually find satisfaction in a private doctor's office.

"I've never gotten any shot at PHS. But I always get a shot at Farmington at $5.00 a shot. It always help to get a shot when you have a cold or a severe headache."

The PHS physicians understandably become frustrated when the casual injection, often given by an office nurse, is regarded so much more highly than their own ministrations.

It is possible that the active immunization programs of some years ago have had their lasting effects. Perhaps patients have derived their zeal for all shots from this source. Another possibility is that receiving a shot satisfies a need of the Navajo for decisive therapy. Another respondent makes this idea explicit:

"We need medicine that are more effective rather than tell the patient to try this certain medicine and come back if it doesn't work."

In the Navajo medical tradition, the practitioner always understood the case. His recommendations were decisive. If the illness was a result of witching, the witch could cause a recurrence of the symptoms, but the patient could reapply for help and be again advised of a definite course of action. The "trial and error" techniques and watchful waiting stance of modern medicine may seem like fumbling to some Navajo patients.

By listening to such complaints about "no shots," we begin to understand the emotional factors which are such an important part of the way any group responds to medical care. With understanding, action can follow. On the one hand educational efforts may be geared towards the uses and abuses of "shots," descriptions of the various types of shots, and information as to why they are administered. Taking another tactic at the same time, during the entire medical process, the personnel may be aware of the danger in approaching the patient in a manner which could be labelled hesitant or unsure.

While the CHR's were polling a group of patients, a medical student stationed in Shiprock was conducting a survey of PHS staff. Again the data was gathered with a questionnaire.* All 170 employees of PHS in Shiprock were part of the sample pool—159 were interviewed by the researcher while the remaining 11 were unavailable at the time of the study. The group of 159 ranged from doctors and nurses to cooks and janitors and included the environmental and field health staff as well as the clinical. In addition, 229 of the questionnaires were sent by mail to all the commissioned officers and supervisory personnel in the Navajo Area. Seventy-eight percent of this mailing group returned their material in time for inclusion in the study. The total number of responses analyzed was 338, 159 from Shiprock and 179 from other parts of the reservation. Two hundred and sixteen of the 338 were supervisory personnel or commissioned officers (primarily white) while 122 were nonsupervisory (primarily Navajo). In all, 109 respondents were Navajo or part Navajo.

Since all Navajos and all commissioned officers are eligible for medical care within the PHS system, we were again interviewing consumers. However, we would have expected our staff-consumers to be a more knowledgeable group.

First the group was asked whether providing health care to Navajos is different from providing it to other low-income groups. This question drew a range of comment. One white physician said:

"Yes, one has a greater empathy since part of their oppression has come from the wrongs of our forefathers and not from their own

----

* For a copy of the questionnaire, see Appendix B.

lack of initiative, laziness, etc."

Other white respondents sensed a lack of appreciation for their services:

"In spite of giving so much, they (the Navajos) don't really like us."

"They are less appreciative than Negroes I have treated. They are less appreciative than Mexican - Americans or narcotic addicts that I have treated at PHS hospital in Fort Worth. They have become so accustomed to "free handouts" that they don't value the expert care that they do get."

A sense of being appreciated is basic to job satisfaction and perhaps explains why those who answered this question at length tended to develop their reply along this tangent. Another white respondent felt that treating Navajos and treating other low income groups are both unrewarding:

"No—they both fall in the same area—no personal relationship—just a job."

The Navajo respondents who answered this question with extended comments tended to look at the situation from the patient's viewpoint. One supervisory employee with some college education who identified himself as part Navajo complained:

"Yes, most of the physicians I have seen assigned to our hospital act as if they are afraid to "touch" the Indian patients. Some even show their disgust by grimaces and verbally."

Or another Navajo respondent:

"First I want to state that I do not know how other low income groups (non-Navajo) are treated. I do know this difference. When I am treated in hospital other than PHS Indian hospital, I am given the time and courtesy as others are given. The difference is probably due to the many patients have to be seen in PHS Indian Hospitals. Clerks and helpers in PHS hospitals are sometimes snotty, probably due to lack of training."

Nonetheless, despite the bitter comments of some Navajos about the kind of treatment they receive, in general the Navajos were more likely than the Anglo employees to deny that legitimate areas of difference exist between treating Navajos and treating other patients. The white supervisory personnel were much more likely to agree with the position and to cite factors such as cultural differences, differences in geographical distribution and isolation, and difference in disease patterns to support their answer. Of 212 supervisory personnel answering this question, only 19 perceived no distinction between Navajo patients and other low income patients. On the other hand, 46 of the 109 Navajos felt no difference.

Speculations can be made about this difference in perception between Navajo and non-Navajo employees. But surely intelligent planning for Navajo health is impossible without recognition of the factors which make the region and its health problems distinctive. Navajo employees are the ones who bear the burden of interpretation between the doctor and the patient. This task cannot be performed satisfactorily without a sense of cultural relativity. Unless Navajos are brought to realize that their health problems are unique and require a unique solution, they are less likely to desire a locally controlled health system. Of course it springs to mind that Navajos living in their own communities do not perceive themselves as "different" but rather as practicing ordinary customs. Still, they must be aware of the premises underlying medical practices around the country in order to cause the system to make the adaptations necessary for the Navajo culture.

Secondly, the participants in the study were asked what type of personnel is in greatest shortage in the Navajo Area. In all groups the need for nurses was strongly felt. The next often mentioned need was for Navajo personnel of all kinds. This opinion was expressed more often by physicians, especially physicians who had remained on the reservation more than two years. Generally, the need for Navajo personnel was most often felt by whites. None of the LPN's, aides, and drivers, all of whom are Navajo, selected this response. Very few respondents cited the need for more and different kinds of ancillary personnel. The man who said we need "paramedicals" because we have "too many chiefs and not enough Indians" was a definite exception.

Thirdly, the employees were asked to suggest changes in present activities which might improve the health of the people the most. The greatest number of suggestions called for a general increase of services. Here the employees resembled the consumers interviewed in the other study—they saw solutions in terms of more beds, a bigger hospital and more personnel. The second ranking suggestion was for more and better health education. The third proposal was to improve communication between patient and staff. One Navajo kitchen worker put it:

"Greet patients with an open heart. Don't show it if you don't like the patient. Make patients feel they are not being neglected."

And another kitchen worker:

"Be kinder to patients to make them happier so they can get well."

These feelings are reminiscent of those of the patients studied by the CHR's. Running through the answers of the nonsupervisory Navajo personnel was a feeling that the doctors at the hospital are not truly qualified.

"This place should not be a training school, we need real doctors."

"Doctors to stay here instead of sending their interns to learn on us."

If employees of the medical system themselves are not aware that PHS physicians are "real doctors," it is not surprising that the average patient shared this misconception.

Not surprisingly, staff members were parochial in their suggestions. Dentists felt the need for more dentists, social workers for better mental health facilities, field health workers for more preventive services.

Interestingly enough, some of the supervisory level personnel were unwilling to suggest what changes might be most needed. Several cited ongoing PHS research and said, "I would leave it to the experts." In sharp contrast is a Shiprock physician, a two-year man, who was willing to suggest a radical course of action. "Curtail services," he wrote, "to emphasize to a lethargic public the general inadequacy of their care."

The final general question called for the employee to name the three most important health needs that are presently inadequately filled. The three areas mentioned the most were health education, environmental health, and maternal and infant health. Nutrition and alcoholism were the next most frequent responses. Among the Navajo subgroup and among the field health subgroup nutrition was mentioned most often as one of the three outstanding problems. Social work and mental health were cited most often by Social Service. The doctors in the study were increasingly likely to highlight mental health problems as their tenure on the reservation increased. Breaking the data down another way, employees from Shiprock and Gallup, the two largest population centers on the reservation, were more likely to focus on mental health problems than those from more rural areas.

The need for a nursing home and care for the chronically ill was more often recognized by aides, LPN's, and drivers. Six percent of Navajos mentioned this need as opposed to only three percent of nonNavajos.

The most interesting result of this exercise in listing is the common omission. Although accidents are the leading cause of adult hospitalization and mortality, they were almost completely ignored by employees asked to rank the three major health problems.

Another method of measuring attitudes offered statements with which the respondent agreed or disagreed. We will not discuss all of these statements but some had very intriguing results.

"The quality of health care provided by the PHS in the Navajo area is adequate." This statement was presented to the employees and only slightly more than half of the people agreed. When the results were broken down into subgroups it was noteworthy that only one-third of the physicians serving the Navajo area felt that the health care was adequate.

"The main reason for Navajos to have poor health is that they don't take care of themselves." This provocative statement was designed to probe a fault-finding attitude towards illness. Among the supervisors, only a .38 agreement rate was found, whereas among nonsupervisors (primarily Navajo) there was a .71 agreement rate. Hazarding reasons for this reaction would merely be a guessing game. Perhaps the employees represent an upwardly mobile segment of the Navajo population who condemn the larger group of patients. Perhaps the supervisors are more conditioned by our Anglo culture to speak kindly of the sick. Or maybe "taking care of themselves" was perceived by the Navajos in terms of the traditional practices in which all illness has a cause, often rooted in the victim's behavior.

The majority of those polled did not agree that "the Navajo people should control the administration of health services on the reservation." The supervisory group favored community control more than the nonsupervisory. The Navajos in the study favored community control 52 percent of the time. Of all groups, physicians were most in favor of community control, perhaps reflecting the liberal attitudes of the "two-year" man who is not dependent on the system.

The employees were asked a multiple choice question about the training of most of the PHS physicians, choosing between 1) have not completed their medical degree, 2) completed degree but have not specialized, 3) are specialists and, 4) are former professors. The correct response, number 2, was recognized by 95 percent of the supervisors. Those who erred did so in the direction of thinking the majority were specialists. Of the nonsupervisors, only

70 percent made the correct response and 10 percent believed the doctors had not completed their training.

The data from this employee study does not give the impression that the Indian Health Service on the Navajo reservation is a well-oiled machine. Rather there are evidences of frustration and conflict. The physicians do not for the most part feel satisfied that the care they render is adequate. The lower level employees are not always sure that the physicians themselves are adequate. Everyone is crying out for more personnel and services, often with an emphasis on the department with which they are most concerned. The Navajo personnel, in a position to be patients themselves, point to the need for improved and pleasanter attitudes of personnel towards patients as a prerequisite for better health conditions. Few imaginative solutions are offered, but the complaints are vivid, energetic, and numerous.

Chapter VI
Infections and Afflictions

In the matter of health problems, the Navajo is a double loser. Diseases typical of an underdeveloped nation flourish on his reservation; for the most part they do not pose a real threat to the United States as a whole. But on the other hand, the Navajos suffer some quite modern health problems which are very much part of urban ghetto life in this decade.

Physicians sometimes refer with a certain nostalgia to the days when infectious diseases ran rampant. In a bizarre way, the infectious disease represented a certain satisfaction for both the doctor and the patient. In an era turbulent with ecology and molecular biology, the bacterial infection is recalled as a comparatively simplistic model of disease and, for the most part, one which is amenable to treatment. The sick child shaking with fever can be restored to an afebrile state after a short course of antibiotic therapy.

Despite the counsel of wiser heads, the decline of infectious disease continues to be attributed to advancements in our pharmacologic armamentarium. But seemingly what is dramatically true for the individual does not necessarily hold true for society as a whole. Dubos and others have pointed out that the decline in infectious disease long antedated the development of antibiotics. The phenomenon was more a product of the social revolution than of improvements in medical technology.

But the Navajo reservation is a medical anachronism in the United States. Tuberculosis and diarrhea still ravage and kill. In 1959, a Cornell study estimated that three-fourths of the illnesses of the Navajo Indians were due to microbial infections, two-thirds of which occurred in persons less than five years old (1). That same year congressional passage of PL 86-121 authorized the Public Health Service to become actively involved in environmental measures to reduce the impact of contagious diseases. Specifically, the PHS was empowered to:

60

construct, improve, extend or otherwise provide and maintain, by contract or otherwise, essential sanitation facilities, including domestic and community water supplies and facilities, drainage facilities, and sewage and waste-disposal facilities, together with necessary appurtenances and fixtures, for Indian homes, communities, and lands.

PHS had accepted the environmental approach to contagious disease. In the first ten years, the program brought safe water and waste disposal facilities to over 54,000 Indian families.

Like the "chicken in every pot" of the 1920's, the slogan of the 1960's was to become a john in every hogan. With the scattered population of the Navajo, however, the task of bringing running water to each home was highly impractical. But to some extent, other forces obviated the problem. Slowly, almost imperceptibly, American history was repeated on the Navajo. Many Indians renounced old living patterns and moved into the larger settlements where jobs were more likely to be available. The break with tradition was by no means complete or universal. Parts of a family squatted in shacks on the fringes of town while other members of the same family remained with their sheep.

Thus a variety of factors have combined to reduce mortality and morbidity for infectious diseases. Social changes were aided by environmental improvements. Mass immunization campaigns protected thousands of children against tetanus, diphtheria, whooping cough, polio and smallpox. For the individual, penicillin and newer antibiotics were available to treat pneumonia, meningitis, and otitis media (middle-ear infections).

Since PHS took over in 1955, many significant improvements have taken place in the health status of the Indian. Infant deaths are down 48 percent. Death rates from gastritis and other diseases of the digestive tract have fallen by 60 percent. And most dramatically, tuberculosis death rates are down by 70 percent.

Yet the problem remains though its dimensions are reduced. Table 1 indicates the discrepancy that exists between the Navajo and the nation. The incidence of these notifiable diseases among the Navajo is ten times higher than the rate for the United States population as a whole. The Indian Health Service realizes that, though it has come a long way in these battles, much is left to be done. To indicate the gaps that remain, the Service has developed a calendar (2) that compares the level of each disease to the appropriate point in time when the general population experienced a similar rate.

Characteristics	Year in which U.S. Rate Approximates Indian 1967 Rate	Difference in Years
Birth rate	No U.S. rate on record is as high as 1967 Indian rate.	
Percentage of live births born in hospital	1962	5
Infant death rate	1947	20
Neonatal	No U.S. rate on record is as low as 1967 Indian rate.	
Postneonatal	1941	26
Maternal death rate		
Using 1967 Indian rate	1964	3
Using 1965-67 avg. rate	1954	12
Age-adjusted death rate, all causes	1941	26
Influenza & pneumonia death rate		
Crude	1945	22
Age-adjusted	1945	22
Diabetes death rate		
Crude	1949	18
Age-adjusted	No U.S. rate on record is as high as 1967 Indian rate.	
Tuberculosis death rate		
Crude	1952	15
Age-adjusted	1950	17
Gastritis, etc., death rate		
Crude	1938	29
Age-adjusted	1941	26
Age expectancy at birth	1939-41 period	27

Another problem which seems incongruous in twentieth century America is malnutrition. Yet malnutrition in both its blatant and subtler forms is a problem on the Navajo reservation.

Demographers have observed that the pattern of childhood death among the Navajo is somewhat different than that found in other developing nations. The time of greatest risk is not immediately after birth but after the first year. Experience in other societies has linked this phenomenon to malnutrition. Indeed, even the flagrant starvation with marked protein deficiencies that constitutes the syndrome of kwashiorkor has been reported among the Navajo (3).

TABLE 1: INCIDENCE OF SELECTED NOTIFIABLE DISEASES*

Disease	Navajo Incidence Per 100,000 Population	General Population U.S. Incidence Per 100,000 Population
Tuberculosis	175	23
Rheumatic Fever	237	2
Streptococcus Infection	7,861	229
Hepatitis	161	21
Measles	172	32
Gonorrhea	2,103	207
Syphilis	329	52
Pneumonia	4,697	Not Reported
Acute Otitis Media	13,611	Not Reported
Chronic Otitis Media	2,108	Not Reported
Gastroenteritis	9,583	Not Reported
Influenza	1,522	Not Reported
Trachoma	1,583	Not Reported

* Bock, G. E., Health Problems, Health Program Deficiencies and Justification for Increased Fiscal Year 1971 Resources, April, 1970 (mimeo.), p. 4.

Malnutrition is probably more prevalent in a subtle way. The chronically under-nourished are more susceptible to a variety of infections and appear to suffer more severely from them. In one carefully conducted study in Guatemala, the health of a village was as much improved by provision of an adequate diet alone as the health of a control village where health treatment was offered. Physical and mental development are linked to food intake. The vicious cycle of poor scholastic performance leading to insufficient education and failure to break out of the poverty culture may need a nutritional as well as an educational attack.

Obtaining food has long been a major preoccupation for the Navajo (4). The staples of his diet were mutton, coffee, and fried bread. The latter is a type of tortilla made from bread dough and cooked in a dry skillet or griddle. Gradually more items were added, including corn meal (usually eaten as a mush) and other cereals. Additional foods had to be purchased from the trading posts, except for a few vegetables which are home grown. Today the Navajos eat a variety of foods depending on their acculturation, income, and the availability of the item.

Certain foods have a meaning for the Navajo beyond their nutritive value. Corn meal is part of many ceremonies. Blue and white corn meal are considered strong foods. Milk is a strong food for babies but not for adults.

And in a society where famine has been known, obesity may be considered a sign of prosperity and good health rather than another form of malnutrition.

Much of the food consumed by the Navajos is purchased from the small trading posts doing credit business with limited selection and high prices. Staple foods—flour, salt, baking powder, lard, corn meal, sugar and coffee—are bought first. Other items are obtained when the family has sufficient credit. In a society with a very low cash economy, the traders are under little pressure to improve their stock or their prices.

The Navajo have evolved a stoic attitude toward food, feasting when it is plentiful and fasting in times of scarcity. Since refrigeration is largely unavailable, perishable foods that are not eaten at once spoil.

In 1958 the tribe instituted a commodity distribution program through an agreement with the state of Arizona. The original project provided only four commodity foods—flour, corn meal, rice, and dry milk—but in subsequent years the program has been expanded. New Mexico and Utah now provide similar programs. Eligibility for the commodity foods is determined by the local county and/or state welfare agencies.

Estimates of the number of Navajos covered in the commodity program range from 60 percent to 70 percent of the population. The current programs aspire to provide about 45 percent of an individual's food needs for a month. Enough food is supplied for 2,600 calories daily for fourteen days of the month, providing all the allocated foods are consumed. Unfortunately, some foods are not fully used by families because the women may not be able to prepare them in a palatable way. Many foods are packaged in bulky containers. With no refrigeration, much of it spoils before it can be eaten.

Two other sources of food have recently been established for high-risk persons. Additional supplies of certain commodity foods are available to families with children under five and to pregnant or lactating women. These supplementary foods are not restricted to those deemed eligible by the welfare department; they are available on the prescription of a doctor or a nurse who certifies that the patient meets the conditions. Finally, a special program for feeding premature infants has been sponsored by the Office of Navajo Economic Opportunity (ONEO). This provides prepackaged milk for each premature infant through the first year of life. Because the babies must be seen by a physician each month before receiving the month's supply, regular medical check-ups are a byproduct.

The effectiveness of both the commodity and the supplemental food programs for the Navajo has been impaired by a series of bureaucratic impediments. Poor administration has left supply depots overstocked with some items and devoid of others. Some foods are not offered in a usable form. For example, milk is highly valued by the Navajo. Condensed milk is used by children and, if available, by adults. But the cans are so large that no family could possibly use it all in one sitting. The mother must opt either to discard an item in scarce supply or to reuse it at the risk of feeding her family spoilt milk.

Powdered milk is provided in the shape of an almost insoluble solid which cannot readily be reconstituted. As a result, the areas around the distribution points take on a powdery appearance as the milk is discarded. Government officials (both federal and tribal) shake their heads over the wasteful indifference of the beneficiaries, but no effort is made to provide better milk powder.

Transportation is also a problem for many families who require the commodity foods most. Since distribution is monthly and the foods are bulky, a vehicle is necessary to get them home. Families who lack a pick-up truck (the only vehicle reliably able to negotiate the rocky terrain and unpaved roads) must sometimes offer a neighbor half their commodities in exchange for his delivery services.

Several programs have been designed to take advantage of the turnout at commodity distribution times. County extension workers and ONEO food demonstrators exhibit ways to utilize the foodstuffs. Public health nurses offer immunizations and health talks. Community workers hold meetings. In many ways a fair-like atmosphere prevails.

As is often the case with such programs, the intent is good but the performance falls short. The deliveries must be more reliable if people are to make the long, expensive trip to the distribution spots. The foods available must conform to the needs of the people rather than the need of the Department of Agriculture to dispose of certain items. Most important, quantities should permit an adequate diet. At the moment, the food programs seem to be premised on the adage, "Half a loaf is better than none." They only aspire to provide 14 day's worth of food each month.

Along with infectious diseases and malnutrition, the Navajo reservation is also plagued by some very modern health problems, including automobile accidents, alcoholism, psychiatric problems, and family planning problems. These latter issues are much harder to approach with programs. At least, when confronted by hunger and contagious disease, PHS personnel were able to formulate some specific plans involving the supply of concrete items—sanitary facilities, immunizations, antibiotics, or food. In the previous pages, we criticized the program for distribution of commodity foods in some of its details. But for the most serious health problems on the reservation—the twin ills of alcoholism and accidents—there really is no program to criticize.

Accidents constitute the leading cause of mortality among adults on the Navajo reservation. By far the greatest expenditure of the Service Unit's contract medical funds goes for special treatment of accident victims, particularly for neurosurgery or orthopedic surgery. The toll which accidents take in death, disability, loss of income and family disruption is staggering. Fifty percent of the 114 accidental deaths and over 20 percent of the 4,803 accident cases seen at a PHS facility were related to motor vehicles (5). In situations in which drunken driving has led to a collision, the lives of survivors and their families may also be shattered by the ensuing legal and psychological repercussions.

The matter of automobile accidents cannot be considered apart from alcoholism. Alcoholism is a major health problem in its own right as well as a large contributor to the hazards of the road.

The white man brought many things with him as he "civilized" the Indian. Smallpox and tuberculosis were in most cases introduced by tragic accident,* but alcohol was used by design. Prior to the arrival of Europeans in the sixteenth and seventeenth century, none of the Indians north of Mexico had any experience with distilled alcoholic beverages. The white man created a market and then exploited it. The alcohol of the trader became an important bargaining tool. The trader also taught the Indian *how* to drink. Inebriation was important if agreements were to favor the trader.

The extent of the alcohol problem is very hard to document, although some suggestive information is available (6). At one PHS facility, alcoholism or its complications accounted for the hospital discharge diagnosis on 4.5 percent of the released patients during a sample period. For males aged 20-44, this proportion rose to 17.4 percent. Scattered reports on alcohol usage by Indians are available but vary in method and quality. Seventy percent of the population over fifteen in one Central Plains reservation reported that they drank. The percentage of drinkers among southwestern Indian tribes varied from 73 percent to 86 percent in the men and 20 percent to 68 percent in the women.

The range of reported estimates is an indication that the problem eludes

---

* It was not always accidental. Peter Farb in his *Man's Rise to Civilization* (E.P. Dutton & Co.; New York, 1968) describes a campaign against Indians waged by British forces during the French and Indian Wars of 1763: "Dogs were not available so officers distributed among the Indians handkerchiefs and blankets from the smallpox hospitals at Fort Pitt—probably the first example of biological warfare in history." p. 248.

systematic study. But nobody doubts its existence. A sixteen-year-old Navajo boy who was part of the Shiprock consumer study described alcoholism as the greatest health problem on the reservation: "Alcoholism causes poor homes, neglected children, unemployment, no food, poor clothing, everything. I really don't know what can be done about it." Neither does the Indian Health Service.

In Shiprock, the same dearth of data on the extent of the alcohol problem prevailed. Arrest statistics in the nearest off-reservation town, however, were revealing; in a Service Unit of some 25,000 Navajos, 2,861 were arrested in one year for drunkenness in the nearby city. While some of these arrests must have been repeated incidents involving the same persons, and while police discrimination probably encouraged the arrests of Indians, the problem is still one of grave magnitude. Another crude measure of alcoholism is usually the prevalence of associated conditions such as cirrhosis of the liver. Interestingly, however, the Navajo drinking pattern of sporadic binges to the point of intoxication does not lead to cirrhosis as frequently as does more chronic sustained inebriation (7).

Legal controls have been the foremost approach to containing the menace. In 1832, Congress, by general statute, banned liquor traffic with the Indians. This prohibition was gradually extended to cover sale, gift, transportation, and possession of liquor on reservations and Indian lands. Specific prohibitions against alcohol were incorporated into treaties and agreements with various tribes.

Although Indians became full citizens in 1924, their prohibition did not end with the rest of the country's in 1933. Congressional anti-liquor laws pertaining to Indians were not repealed until 1953. A number of tribal councils, including the Navajo, have maintained the prohibition up to the present time. Each year the question of legalizing liquor on the Navajo reservation is raised, discussed, and defeated in tribal council. The Indian Health Service has not taken a position in the debates.

The liquor laws aggravate the dangers of alcohol. On the Navajo reservation, the penalty for transporting liquor is more severe than for driving while intoxicated. The preferable alternative, therefore, is to transport one's alcohol internally. Since (except for bootleggers) the only source of liquor is in stores off the reservation, drunken driving is prevalent.

Those charged with the health of the Indian have recognized the need to attack the alcohol issue. The Task Force on Alcoholism has gone on record to state:

The Indian Health Service considers alcoholism to be one of the most significant health problems facing the Indian and Alaskan Native people today. Probably no other condition so adversely affects so many aspects of Indian life in the United States. It is the policy of the Indian Health Service that services and programs for the prevention and comprehensive treatment of alcoholism be given the highest possible priority at all levels of administration (8).

The Task Force outlines a comprehensive program of direct personal services (including general medical, psychiatric, social services, and nursing), rehabilitation and training, health education, community involvement, research and evaluation.

Priorities for planning are not always priorities for funding. The reality is a fragmented, piecemeal service with little built-in evaluation. The comprehensive plan of the Alcohol Task Force was a good standard approach but unfortunately no nurses, social workers, health educators, doctors and so on were assigned specifically to that purpose. In most Service Units the daily demands for patient care make health workers reluctant to take on the alcoholic. The demands are too great and the rewards too few. Some scattered programs do exist, usually sponsored by an interested social worker or physician. Antabuse has been widely utilized on the Navajo reservation with varying success. Glowing reports can often be shown to be based on the preselection of good candidates. Few carefully controlled studies have been conducted to test specific treatment programs.

The rehabilitation of the alcoholic is a difficult task anywhere and there is no reason to suspect it should be any easier on the Navajo reservation. Moreover, on the reservation the problem is complicated by prohibition. The various religious denominations which originally worked to convert the Navajo have left a lasting mark on a large segment of the population. Drinking is considered sinful to religious Navajos. The pronounced Mormon influence on the reservation reinforces this judgment. Social drinking has never been part of the Navajo culture and, given prohibition and widespread moral repugnance towards alcohol, present drinking habits are not soon to be channelled into less destructive patterns.

Clearly, the alcoholism is part (and a large part) of the mental health problems of the reservation. Widespread unemployment, the growing family break-up, and the general feelings of depression linked with lack of opportunity may be combined with alcoholism. Among Indians, homicides run about three to four times the national average, and suicides have been about one and a half times the rate for United States residents of all races (9). In addition, many suspect that unreported suicides are sometimes committed by automobile. Currently, attention has been focused on the disastrous emotional impact of the standard BIA school on young people—the young people who are the promise of the future. The mental health teams have been pulled in many directions at once, with increasing demands for their services. They have sought to utilize local workers and even traditional medicine men as therapists.

The PHS cannot be criticized for its failure to come up with the definitive cure for alcoholism. The answer is not available and the only hope for a solution is in continued experimentation. But PHS can be blamed for not making a concentrated and vigorous effort to reduce drunken driving and accidents.

In moments of discouragement we have thought that, in order to make an impact on mortality statistics, we should manage a bar in Shiprock. Behind this flippant position, a truth lurks. Alcohol-related accidents are perhaps the major health problem, accounting for unnecessary death. disability, and family disruption. Imbibers sometimes have to drive over 50 miles on dark unpaved roads to get to their drink. Yet the PHS takes no position on the legalization of alcohol.

Despite the fact that a statement on the issue would be controversial, we feel that PHS evades its responsibility by remaining silent. The question is very much a health problem. Our own bias is to feel that legalization of liquor would bring the problem under greater local control, perhaps encourage a tendency towards drinking at home, and help reduce automobile accidents. But a case may be made for the opposite position; it could be argued that bringing liquor closer to home might further disrupt the mental health of families, expose young children to violence from drunks and temptations to start drinking. The point is that the Indian Health Service should have the expertise in various disciplines to make an educated decision and then have the courage to announce it. Health leadership is not consistent with sitting on a fence.

Even without legalization, PHS could advocate stricter controls of the drunken driver. The police might be supplied with and trained in the use of breathanalyzers. The cost of this equipment could be borne appropriately by PHS if no other source were available. After all, the cost of one hospital day prevented is almost equal to the cost of a machine. No effort should be spared to separate the drunk and his vehicle.

In the Shiprock Area, pedestrians are also in danger because of the location of the bars right on the major highways. In addition, animals graze freely along the roads so that automobiles are likely to collide with horses, cows, and sheep as well as inebriated strollers. In our Service Unit, we initiated experiments with retroreflective materials to reduce night-time road accidents. The project, aimed to protect man and beast, involved affixing a piece of retroreflective material to the animal to render him visible for long distances at night. The same principle could be applied to pedestrians. We have toyed with the thought of asking the owners of the several bars which delineate the reservation borders to affix a piece of retroreflective tape to each departing customer.

Driver education is another approach to the accident problem which could be utilized more heavily. Stress might be placed on use of seat-belts, periodic check of automobiles, and safety rules for passengers in the back of a truck. Too often one observes children perched on the top of wobbly loads in an open truck, despite the tragic accidents which occur every year for this reason.

From the tragedy of alcoholism and accidents which cut off the Navajo people in their prime, we turn to another difficult problem in a sensitive area, namely population control.

From a band of about 7,000 when they left Fort Sumner, the Navajo Nation has grown to over 100,000 people. (From observation of the way the 1970 census was taken on the reservation, we have every reason to believe that the Navajo were undercounted.) In earlier years, population growth was crucial to survival of the tribe and its people. In many agrarian societies, children are a form of economic protection. They guarantee a pool of manpower for maintaining and enlarging one's holdings; they are a source of protection and support when the parents can no longer work. With high rates of infant mortality, large numbers of offspring are needed to ensure that several will survive to adulthood.

With improvements in health, the need for having large families in order to maintain the population is less pressing. In a more affluent system, children become a liability rather than an asset as the period of dependency is prolonged by compulsory education. The economic status of the Navajo has left them vulnerable on several counts. The children are a dependent burden, and jobs are already insufficient for adults in a land that is unable to support its population without imported foodstuffs.

Family planning sometimes conjures up alarming images of test-tube babies in a brave new world. To many Navajos, the concept of family planning is even more fearsome. It is associated with extinction as a people, genocide. The tension runs close to the surface when Navajos discuss this issue. Many interpret efforts along the family planning line as an attempt to breed the race into oblivion. Other Indian tribes have virtually disappeared because of declining birth rates in the face of captivity and inhospitable government reservations.

The data suggests, however, that Navajos are continuing to increase in numbers. In 1968 the crude Navajo birthrate was 37 births per 1,000 people compared to a United States figure of about 19. Half the children born were the fourth or more sibling in the family (the median order of birth was 4.0) and, more startling, almost ten percent of the mothers had borne ten or more babies.

How then does one establish a family planning program in a setting of suspicion and misunderstanding? The problem is relatively new for PHS; birth control as an active program began in 1964 (10). One key to success must be personal contact and ability to convince the consumer of genuine concern for his welfare. The consumer must have confidence that the system works in his best interest—and also that it works properly. While infant mortality has been reduced dramatically, the Navajo infant death rate for 1968 was still 49.7 per 1,000 live births, more than twice the United States rate for 1967 of 22.4 per 1,000 live births. These statistics must continue to be improved before we can expect the Navajo consumer to accept planned families. After all, there can be no planning if the patient cannot also plan on his children's likely survival.

Good medical care, in the sense of being comprehensive and continuous, must be the first step in family planning. An appropriate target group would be the mothers of young children. At present, over 95 percent of babies are born in hospitals. Personalized care of the mother during her prenatal course and confinement together with a program of active well baby care should produce an audience more receptive to the arguments for family planning.

A pilot program to test the validity of this hypothesis has recently been developed on the Shiprock Service Unit. Using registered nurses with advanced training in midwifery as the primary purveyors of care under the supervision of an obstetrician, the project has sought as its first objective high quality, personal obstetrical care. Funding is currently being sought to support a cadre of community workers to extend the program beyond the hospital.

Reports from other Service Units would suggest that family planning efforts have been about as successful with the Indian population as with most other groups. In a study on another part of the Navajo reservation at Tuba City, 42 percent of the women enrolled in an oral contraception program discontinued after one to thirteen months. This rate is somewhat greater than found in other parts of the country. Overall, 39 percent of women who delivered in Indian Health Service hospitals accepted birth control services within two months after discharge. The comparable overall rate for United States hospitals is 45 percent. Unfortunately, no long-term follow up is available for either study (10).

In the last analysis, it is appropriate for the Navajos to decide themselves, as communities and as individual families, to what extent they wish to endorse a family planning approach. It is not appropriate for PHS to decide. But it is the responsibility of PHS to provide the information and tools to allow patients to control the size and spacing of their families if they desire. Because of the extreme sensitivity of the issue, we feel that the information can only be effectively delivered in the context of a personal relationship and with the full understanding that the parents must make the choice. Once the lack of pressure or moral judgment is perceived, many women are likely to express an interest in at least spacing their children so that they will be better able to provide materially and emotionally for the whole family.

Poor housing conditions throughout the reservation constitute a problem closely related to health. Estimates made in 1969 concluded that there are about 20,000 Navajo homes, of which 48 percent have only one room and 78 percent have two rooms or less. Only 19.7 percent of homes have refrigeration, 21.4 percent have running water, and 25.6 percent have electricity. Even fewer homes have flush toilets or thermostatically controlled heat.

In Shiprock the problem was aggravated by growing industrialization. Housing was simply not available in the town to accommodate the employees of a new local plant, the Fairchild Corporation, particularly the single women. At best, the people accepted crowded trailer-court conditions which are inconsistent with the Navajo life-style. At worst, the residences were unsafe.

On February 19th, 1970, the *Navajo Times* ran an exposé entitled "Shameful Scenes at Shiprock." The newspaper pointed to the fact that "families and single people are living in tents and tar paper shacks in order to continue working." Quoting from the article:

The grim circumstances of single housing here was tragically punctuated recently by the death of two Fairchild single women by carbon monoxide poisoning. The vehicle of death was a trailer far beyond its point of safe service as a home. Girls walk, hitchhike and commute long distances because there is no place to live. Two lost their lives in an auto accident in 1969.

Industry continues to circumvent Shiprock as they become aware of the inadequate housing potential for employees and management staff. Fairchild is the oldest industrial plant on the reservation. They have been in Shiprock since 1965. There has been a constant struggle for adequate housing since their first trainees were put on the job. If we expect industrial development and a standard of living with a minimal level of decency we must have adequate housing. An apartment complex for single women would be a major step towards progress on this essential area of man's needs—shelter.

Seemingly, health planners are simultaneously faced with the problems of isolation of rural inaccessible areas and the problems of supplying services for growing industrialized areas. The latter is a newer role for health authorities on the Navajo reservation.

In the course of my tenure as a Service Unit director at Shiprock, I felt it entirely appropriate to spend time consulting with the management of the large local industry about methods to combat some of the glaring problems. The Fairchild Corporation is planning to construct housing facilities complete with a shopping center and this step should help alleviate the housing shortage. At the same time, local PHS officials at the Service Unit extended every cooperation to a private agency which was developing a day-care center to accommodate the children of working mothers. At times the Service Unit is so busy with its regular tasks that it is hard to free personnel for new projects. Yet aspects such as housing and child care in an increasingly industrialized area are probably as vital to physical and mental well-being as periodic check-ups and immunizations.

On a more optimistic note, the Indian does seem to have avoided some of the chronic disease problems of the white man. Studies suggest that the rates of such killers as arteriosclerotic heart disease and cancer are lower among Indian populations. One is, however, tempted to attribute part of the discrepancy to inadequate diagnosis and failure to seek out the disease in question. Some chronic diseases do seem to favor Indian hosts. Diabetes, defined in terms of abnormal glucose metabolism, is quite common among southwestern Indians, but it seems to be a different disease in some respects. Complications of diabetes in the kidney, eyes, and arteries are seen with less frequency among the Navajo than in the general population. Elevated blood sugars seem to be better tolerated by the Indian. It was not unusual to find Navajos walking around comfortably with blood sugar levels so high that one would surely have expected the patient to be in diabetic coma (11).

There is one chronic disease, however, which the Indian suffers more severely than the white. This is cholecystitis and cholelithiasis (gall bladder disease). Rates among southwestern Indians are generally in excess of white rates. Most theories to explain this implicate the high fat diet.

Indians in Oklahoma who have largely adopted white ways and have readier access to medical centers suffer more frequently from obesity, diabetes, hypertension, and gall bladder pathology than do the Indians of the Southwest (12). This data may well be the result of better reporting. Speculation about the reasons for the Navajo escape from many chronic diseases supports epidemiologic theories about the relationship between life style and disease. We can anticipate that as the Indian becomes more acculturated he will inherit the right to heart attacks, strokes, and cancer. Evidence for this hypothesis is already available.

The control of chronic disease in any population requires a rethinking of our approach. We have already noted that the dangers of infectious disease among the Indians, although still present, are declining rapidly. The Public Health Service should be ready for the change of emphasis.

In chronic disease treatment, as cure gives way to care, the physician finds himself in a new and somewhat strange role of helping the patient cope with rather than recover from his affliction. Public health personnel will be seeking ways to encourage, persuade, or coerce society to alter its behavior in areas that have become fixed. Communication with the patients, as individuals and as consumer groups, will become more important than it was for successful immunization programs.

Sitting around a cigarette-littered conference table plotting a strategy to improve techniques in health education, we deplore the fact that Navajos do not follow health advice. Successful health education produces a change in behavior. Our own example with cigarettes illustrates how difficult it is to motivate genuine behavior change. The threat of impending doom in the distant future is not potent enough to get us to change a fixed habit today.

Preventive efforts in other countries have shown that the preventive services are more acceptable when coupled with curative ones. But these preventive programs were still focused on a relatively simple behavioral change such as winning over a patient to accept immunization. In that instance, the individual need be persuaded only once and material quickly conveyed through a syringe or a pill confers on him lifelong immunity against an illness. But how do we protect against recurring problems for which we know no immunological mechanism? Feeding a child prevents malnutrition today but the threat arises anew tommorow. Seat-belts must be worn every time. Cigarette smoking must be permanently eliminated.

Perhaps the frustration in trying to bring about behavior modifications account for our susceptibility to the enticement of modern technology. With wonder and confidence, we look at a morass of tubes and computer components which can produce a myriad of data to indicate physiologic or biochemical deficiencies. Early disease detection and multiphasic screening have been accepted into the core of medicine as part of the technological revolution. But data that cannot lead to meaningful action is of little practical value. Where is the point in early disease detection if nobody can motivate the patient to take the necessary steps to reduce the threat against him?

No sophisticated equipment is required to identify gross obesity. Epidemiologic data confirm that overweight is a threat to health on many fronts. But changing the eating habits of Americans (including Navajos) is a formidable task. One social commentator has said that, by popularizing the concept of the Slim Generation, the Pepsi Cola Company is doing more to promote health than the AMA.

The medical professions in general recognize that the spectrum of disease has shifted to the chronic illnesses, yet personnel have not been trained to help people to cope. Medical school curricula emphasize diagnosis of the esoteric. We have developed cadre upon cadre of technicians and aides but nobody to spend time with the patient, to share his concerns and allay his fears. Instead, each subspecialty focuses on a single aspect of the problem. The American medical machine has become proficient in monitoring and measuring but has lost the art of communicating.

The renaissance of the family doctor across the United States is the result of the growing depersonalization of the medical system. Better defined, better trained, and better certified, the new-old specialty of family medicine represents organized medicine's reaction to consumer pressure for a figure with whom to relate.

The Indian Health Service has a little extra time to prepare for the onslaught of the chronic diseases. Already, with longer life expectancy and growing acculturation, an Indian is more likely to fall victim to a chronic disease than he was 20 years ago. On the Navajo reservation the break-up of the extended family has caused some consumers to call for more nursing home facilities. The Indian Health Service has the option of waiting, as did medicine as a whole, until the outcry becomes a clamor, or planning ahead to face a growing problem.

The barriers to communication raised by language and culture among

Indian groups pose greater problems when the patient requires supportive help to live with a chronic problem and alter his behavior patterns accordingly. In subsequent chapters, we will discuss possible approaches to manpower problems, including the development of Navajo nonphysician practitioners as primary figures in rendering care. Such a solution makes even more sense when the health problem is chronic (such as heart disease), social and environmental (such as accidents and family planning), or both (such as alcoholism).

Logically, the Indian Health service should be able to shift its focus more easily than private institutions which operate on a profit motive and respond only to highly articulated consumer demands. Unfortunately, even new public institutions seem quickly to become masters of their own inventors. In days when the newspapers regularly speak of a national health corps, serious study should be given to determine whether such institutions can remain responsive to current needs. It would be ironical to organize yet another bureaucracy, in response, say, to the urban ghetto problems of addiction, only to be left with an unadaptable mechanism long after drug traffic disappears.

The Indian Health Service could be a good indicator of what we can expect from a health bureaucracy. It will be instructive to observe whether the Indian Health Service is able to mobilize itself to attack some of the social health-related problems in a concerted way and to prepare itself for the advent of the chronic disease.

REFERENCES

1. McDermott, W. K. *et al.* Interim report on Indian health to the Commission on Rights, Liberties, and Responsibilities of the American Indian, June 20, 1959, p. 83 (mimeo).
2. Gaps between health status of Indians and Alaska natives and the U. S. population. Memorandum from Chief, Program Analysis and Statistics Branch, to Director, Indian Health Service, January 5, 1970.
3. Van Duzen, J. *et al.* Protein and caloric malnutrition among preschool Navajo Indian children. *American J. Clin. Nutrition,* 1969, *22,* 1362-78.
4. The discussion is based on the work of McDonald, Barbara S. *Nutrition of the Navajo.* (2nd ed.) 1965 (mimeo).
5. Brown, *et al.* The epidemiology of accidents among the Navajo Indians. Public Health Reports, 1970, *85,* 881-88.
6. Alcoholism: A high priority heath problem. Report of the Indian Health Service Task Force on Alcoholism, Section One, December, 1969 (mimeo).
7. Kunitz, A. J. *et al.* Alcoholic cirrhosis among the Navajo. *Quart. J. Stud. Alcohol* 1969, *30,* 672-85.
8. Indian Health Service Task Force on Alcoholism, *op. cit.,* p. 1.

9. Ogden, M. *et al.* Suicides and homicides among Indians. *Public Health Reports,* 1970, *85,* 75-80.
10. Rabeau, I. S. & Reaud, A. Evaluation of PHS program providing family planning services for American Indians. *Amer. J. Pub. Health,* 1969, *59,* 1331-38.
11. Saiki, J. H. & Rimion, D. L. Diabetes mellitus among the Navajo. *Arch. Int. Med.* 1968, *122,* 1-5.
12. McDermott, W. K., *op. cit.,* p. 4.

Chapter VII

A Service Unit in Search of a Program

The Service Unit is the action point in the federal government's most extensive attempt to provide medical care to a civilian population. The policies formulated in Washington are enacted or not enacted here. The bureaucrats and resource people in Washington and in the Area offices exist to support and enable what happens at the Service Unit level. Understanding of Indian Health Service calls for close examination of this unit of service. In this chapter, we will be describing the Shiprock Service Unit with which we are most familiar. Since all Service Units share the same superstructure, with the same pool for personnel and the same methods of funding and planning, the problems of one mirror those of another.

The Shiprock Service Unit includes sections of three states, Arizona, New Mexico, and Utah. Its relatively well-defined boundaries encompass approximately 25,000 persons in 5,000 square miles. For this population, it is the primary source of medical care, providing inpatient, outpatient, emergency, pharmacy, dental, optometric, field health, preventive, school health, and environmental health services. The Service Unit is also the principal third-party sponsor for much of the medical care rendered to Navajos in the surrounding community hospitals and at referral centers.

At the time of writing, the Shiprock Service Unit included a 75-bed hospital with an out-patient department that handled approximately 5,000 patient visits per month in the hospital clinic and four field clinics. The staff included twelve physicians (an internist, a pediatrician, an obstetrician, a surgeon, seven general medical officers and the Service Unit director), 18 RN's, 15 LPN's, and 14 nursing assistants. Four public health nurses, each with a driver-interpreter, worked under the supervision of the director of the field health nursing program. The dental program was staffed by three dentists, each with two dental assistants; two of the dentists conducted clinics in boarding schools. Also serving the school population was one optometrist. Three school nurses covered the over 3,000 children in BIA boarding schools in the region. Complete pharmacy services were provided through four pharmacists. Two sanitarians and three sanitary engineers supervised routine environmental surveillance activities and were instrumental in developing new water resources for a desert population. Two health educators worked with both the field health and hospital health staffs. One social worker and one social work assistant serviced the entire Service Unit.

The total staff of the Service Unit numbered about 170 persons, many of whom occupied roles in administration, personnel, medical records, maintenance, dietary, housekeeping, supplies and laboratory.

A few statistics will dramatize the shortages. While the United States per capita health expenditure is reported in excess of $300, Shiprock spends only $65 per capita. In Shiprock there are 92 professional nurses per 100,000 people as compared to 331 per 100,000 for the nation. Similarly the Shiprock ratio of physicians is 48 per 100,000 compared to 125 nationally. Not surprisingly, those laboring under such scarcities feel, like the Red Queen, that all their energies are required just to remain in the same place.

The challenge was to develop programs to meet the needs of the Navajo community while coping with shortages. Our immediate goal was to create an atmosphere in which personnel might lose their fear of innovation at a local level. The following pages will describe the failures in approach along with the successes. Effort should be discussed as well as achievement, for without the former there is little chance of the latter. The time period covered is just one year. Some of the projects have yet to reach fruition.

A number of problems required simultaneous attention, but perhaps foremost was the need to convince the staff that changes were possible. Although an avalanche of memoranda from headquarters over the past few years had emphasized the importance of staff involvement in planning at the local level, rarely did it happen. More often each department within the Service Unit was caught up in its own problems and frustrations. The departments tended to be indifferent or defensively antagonistic when their needs interfered with each other. Unfortunately this attitude of isolation discouraged the individual departments from examining their problems in other than a "more of the same" way. A sense of impotence held sway. It was believed that decisions would be made either higher up locally or at the Area level. Capable people had moved from a sense of futility to lethargy.

In an attempt to break down the isolation of the departments, general staff meetings were instituted on a twice monthly basis. They were more than a forum for general announcements. At each meeting one department head was responsible for outlining that department's activities, the problems it was facing, and the programs it would like to see developed to meet its needs. The presentations became the focus of general discussion by other department heads. As the year progressed the notes taken at these meetings formed the basis for the Service Unit program plan.

The stress was continually on searching for new ways to do things. Each department was urged to identify other sources of funds outside the traditional restricted budget, and other ways to cover the costs of a particular project. Understandably, for many the challenge of suddenly looking outside the Public Health Service was overwhelming, but in some departments the exercise paid off. A pharmacy department auditing project, for example, sought financial support through a grant from one of the drug companies. Application for this grant was handled entirely from within the pharmacy department, and brought with it a sense of buoyancy and power in place of the old impotence which PHS employees generally feel. To the other departments, this was an illustration of an accomplishment outside of the routine lock-step method.

One of the consistent areas of friction lay between medical personnel who provided direct services and the field health staff who were responsible for a variety of public health and preventive programs. Because the field health work is an attempt to arouse the patient's concern about a problem rather than a response to concerns which the patient already feels, this group enjoyed more freedom to plan its work than did the providers of care. The providers always felt besieged by hordes of patients with unmet needs. The difference in apparent output led to considerable conflict between the two factions. The providers resented the leisurely pace of the field health staff and clamored for transfer of nurses to the hospital service. In turn the field health unit was threatened by the spectre of loss of identity and transformation into direct providers. Talking with both sides and helping them to appreciate the merits and importance of both approaches required much effort. No preventive program can gain acceptance unless curative services are available. Yet curative treatment is a never ceasing problem unless efforts are made to change life-styles and eliminate those elements which contribute to disease.

As the field health staff became more confident that discussions of the issues were not tantamount to imposed changes, it became less defensive and more willing to look at itself objectively. The director of field health nursing began to analyze the staff members' records to determine how and on whom their efforts had been spent.* Discussions and experimentation began on ways

---

* These studies were important management tools for use within the Service Unit to

to improve communications between the two areas. Field health personnel initiated cost-benefit analysis of their own activities. Eventually a new structure emerged which offered the providers more involvement in the field health programs in exchange for freeing some field health staff for clinical work.

The clinical staff, for its part, was also examining its programs. The medical staff was fortunate in having several physicans who were not only well trained but also well motivated.

The hospital was already using a more sophisticated system of medical records called "Problem Orientation." Developed by Dr. Lawrence Weed (1), this method focuses attention on the reason for any given action by linking it to a problem identified in the patient. The patient's problems and the state of their definition is kept in the clinician's attention by a problem list at the front of each chart. The new physicians enthusiastically adopted the Problem Oriented Record, despite the fact that, for some, the conversion involved changing fairly entrenched habits.

As frustrations with the inadequacy of actual care grew, discussions turned to ways to identify the deficits and remedy them. Gradually the physicians began to recognize that, while many of the daily difficulties could be attributed to the pressures of the patient load and the shortage of supplies, changes in their own behavior could help to overcome the handicaps. At first minor but important administrative changes were made to facilitate patient care. An appointment system was established and patients were encouraged to return to the same doctor who could then provide more continuous care.

The clinical staff developed a basic set of data which they felt necessary to follow a patient over the years. This information was designed to document important changes in his health status. Items for inclusion were carefully scrutinized to make sure they justified the time and effort. (For example, our single x-ray machine was already performing at three times the recommended capacity and could not sustain any additional burdens.) Eventually, after consultation with nursing personnel, a list of screening items which would form a data base was developed and the assignments for acquiring the information distributed between physicians and nurses. The form was printed and placed on each chart opposite the problem list.

---

identify which nursing districts were not performing well. But they were also important for the whole Service in documenting the high cost of travel and paperwork time (a third or more of the total) and of uncompleted home visits (a quarter of all visits). These data supported the use of persons other than a nurse for much of the home visiting and formed a basis for discussions with Area personnel on the need to revamp field health priorities.

Perhaps the most significant step taken by the medical staff was the development of an active and unique program of medical auditing. As required of every accredited hospital, Shiprock had a standing audit committee which met monthly to determine whether the level of care in the hospital was adequate. As interest grew in taking positive steps to improve patient care, however, this perfunctory system of auditing proved inadequate and ineffectual. In its place the staff developed an intensive program of review. All physicians became responsibile for the audit of the charts belonging to patients currently under treatment. Where deficiencies were found, immediate corrective action could be implemented.

Each physician on the staff reviewed approximately four charts each month. The charts were those of patients randomly selected as they were admitted to the hospital or seen in the clinics. Using the principles of problem orientation, the auditor asked four basic questions: 1) Were all the necessary data gathered? 2) Were all the patient's problems indentified? 3) Were the problems appropriately and adequately acted upon? 4) Was there a plan indicated for necessary follow-up?

A note was dictated on the basis of these answers and submitted to the audit committee. Any defects were immediately brought to the attention of the colleague responsible for the patient. Each month the collected audits were summarized and reviewed by the entire medical staff to note recurring problems. These problem areas became the focus of the postgraduate education programs to correct that behavior.

Such a program relies heavily on the cooperation and interest of the record librarian. She is responsible for selecting the charts for review and compiling the audit reports. When specific disease entities are sought for postgraduate programs, she identifies the appropriate charts. Throughout she must be an active and vital member of the review group. We have found that in general employees have welcomed the opportunity to become part of an interesting project and to exercise their skills to a fuller degree, even if it entails more work for them or their department. This was certainly true of the record librarian in the case of the auditing effort.

This program of auditing is virtually unique in the nation. At a time when most medical staffs across the country are loath to engage in any sort of peer review, this system demonstrates that quality medicine may be pursued in an atmosphere of shortages of men, money, and materials.

Gradually the auditing program expanded. Pharmacists developed a similar audit guide to review the use of drugs. They developed a drug profile for each patient which became part of the screening form. Nursing was invited to discard its traditional nursing notes and contribute as an active member of the team in the "progress note" section more traditionally reserved for the physician.

Another problem was identified early—the ubiquitous issue of poor communication between the doctor and patient. As physicians gained experience with the Navajo culture, they recognized that interpreters drafted from aides and clerks varied widely in how they expressed things. Certain aides would avoid the interpreter duties when the subject was one they either did not understand or preferred not to discuss. Others would simply omit to ask questions which were an essential part of the medical history.

This vexing problem was attacked in several different ways. Noontime interpreter classes were held on an elective basis. These classes, conducted by a physician and a health educator who were both Navajo speaking, covered introductory material on anatomy, pathology, and general medicine in bilingual sessions. Often the discussions would turn to how one would translate a particular concept. Though these sessions were generally popular, the hectic hospital routine drew the aides and clerks into a conflict of interest. While their supervisors recognized the need for the interpreter classes, the work in their job descriptions also had to be performed. Attendance dropped slowly; classes began to start later.

Many employees began to think of a formal interpreter training program as a desirable goal. At the same time the need for better communication within the Service Unit staff between the several departments was recognized. A plan gradually evolved to curtail Service Unit clinical activities for one-half day a week and devote that time to training and communication. Over six months was needed to contact each of the Chapters in the Service Unit region and explain the reasons for restricting services in this way. Overwhelmingly, the point that sold the idea to these consumer groups was the hope of better translations. From an idea and a booklet in November, the half-day closing became a reality in June.

The half-day closing may seem an odd decision for an overloaded facility to make. Yet the staff of the Service Unit desperately needed to stop and think, to talk to each other and plan. When the issue was put to the consumers, they too were willing to sacrifice quantity in the hope of a higher quality in the future.

A third solution was proposed to assist in communication with the patients. Part of the problem involved obtaining an accurate medical history. To facilitate history taking, a list of questions similar to the review of symptoms in a complete medical evaluation was developed for a variety of problems. From the chief complaint, the interpreter could go on to gather the basic information about the patient and present the package to the physician. Thus the physician did not need to be present for the basic history and the interview could be conducted without the constraints that simultaneous interpretation imposes. Standard translations of each question were planned, the exact wordings to be worked out in the interpreter classes.

Beyond the language barrier, other obstacles disturbed doctor-patient communication. As we became aware of the consumer attitudes as displayed by the CHR study, we recognized that one basic mission was education of the public about the Service Unit, its staff and its problems. Discussions with small groups of consumers at Chapter meetings and on other occasions led us to believe that the Navajos could understand and accept the PHS better when explanations were carefully offered. The reasons behind the discriminate use of shots could be outlined or the physician's training described with gratifying results. Because of the high illiteracy rate, communication had to be verbal; because of the vast distances and scattered population in the area, a surer route to the consumer than meetings in small groups was required.

In this age of television, our answer was refreshingly old-fashioned—the radio! Since many Navajos pick up their mail only sporadically and do not have regular access to a newspaper, the Navajo-speaking broadcasts on the local radio stations are the major means of communication. News of local interest and announcements of coming events are as important as entertainment. The significance of the radio in the life of the Navajo is illustrated by the fact that the chairman of the Navajo tribe at that time, Raymond Nakai, first became known to his constituents when he was employed as a Navajo language radio announcer in Flagstaff, Arizona.

To tap this captive audience, we worked with the health educators to develop a series of five-minute taped programs in Navajo. These were aired by the local radio station closest to the Service Unit during its regular Navajo language broadcasts. The scripts were written by different members of the staff and covered a variety of topics. The reasons for delays at the clinic were explained. Brief biographical sketches of personnel emphasized their training and sought to personalize the staff. The broadcasts offered information on common health problems and even tried to explain why shots were not administered on all occasions.

The role of the medical consumer had customarily been that of a passive recipient, dubious and distrustful but occasionally protesting some outrage. The Navajo politician generally acted as go-between, working with the Service Unit administration to try to get something more for the people, while assuring his constituents that they were being protected. Needless to say, the Service Unit director, who did not speak the language, was not encouraged by such a system to gain contact with the consumer, or they with him. Yet there was a great need for just this sort of contact.

We did meet with groups both formally and informally to talk with them about the health situation. In each discussion we sought to put health in its proper perspective beside the other deprivations the Navajos faced, but each time we stressed the serious lacks of funding and manpower under which we operated. We sought to turn animosity away from the innocent providers and to channel aggression against the system that was responsible. A small handbook of facts was developed about the Service Unit and its shortages. This fact sheet became a political weapon in the hands of those working to improve the health situation.

The Service Unit director was able to engage in these community efforts only because, as a two-year man himself, his future was not linked to PHS. He thought of himself as personally expendable and indeed, perhaps not coincidentally, was transferred to a "planning" position outside the Indian Health Service for the second year of his PHS committment. At the outset, he was aware that he had two years at the most to urge change and that perhaps after his departure the momentum would slip. Such thinking could easily become a rationalization for inactivity, yet the dilemma is real. The two-year man can afford to challenge the system but will not have time to make many durable reforms. The career man has nothing but time on his hands but rarely does he feel able to take the personal risks. The problem is a two-edged sword, with the scabbard nowhere in sight. Perhaps, if such an alliance were possible, a dual leadership of the careerist and two-year man would be the most effective, with the end result being changes that are less sweeping but more permanent. This is a very pertinent question for any large federal health program—how can the personnel be given genuine freedom to challenge the system without a loss in security?

Meanwhile we also tried to apply ourselves directly to the problem of manpower shortages. In this area the efforts met with varying degrees of success; some attempts have been already relegated to the shelf of "good tries."

Since the fluctuation of available physicians is linked to the status of the draft, this source of manpower tends to ebb and flow with our country's military commitments. At best we have large numbers of transients; at worst we cannot fill all our positions. Yet much of the disease seen in the outpatient department is of a relatively simple nature, the diagnosis and treatment of which can be rather well defined. When we analyzed our outpatient diagnostic pattern, almost 40 percent of the visits were diagnosed in one of six categories: pharyngitis (including strep throat), upper respiratory infections, impetigo, otitis media, conjunctivities, and gastroenteritis. Persons other than a physician could readily be trained to handle the first four of these problems together with other routine examinations such as physicals and screening examinations.

As an immediate response to the overwhelming clinic load, we experimented with the use of pharmacists to dispense directly those medicines which could ordinarily be purchased in any drugstore without a prescription. Using a careful set of screening items to detect serious pathology, the pharmacists were empowered to offer symptomatic treatment for adults with a variety of common ailments such as cold, headaches, impetigo, and flu. A taped announcement in both Navajo and English explained the program at regular intervals to those persons waiting at the clinic. Patients could elect to avoid long delays—often in excess of three hours just to get a bottle of aspirin—and see a pharmacist for immediate treatment.

The experiment was a failure. In three months of operation, we had only a handful of takers. Perhaps such an innovation required more extensive education and preparation of the patient population. In any event, the patients who came to see a doctor perceived a visit to the pharmacist as something less desirable and preferred to wait their turn.

The introduction of physician surrogates raises a basic point in consumer relations. Experience with the use of nurse practitioners in Kansas (2) and Colorado (3) and the role of the Medex physician assistant in the state of Washington (4) has repeatedly demonstrated that professionals other than doctors are accepted by patients and not infrequently preferred. They can communicate more readily with the patient and offer him more time and attention. The consumer, who always seeks care as well as cure, reacts most positively.

The advantages of such a program, however, are not usually apparent to the patient *a priori* and this aspect poses a dilemma in consumer relations. Few patients, offered a choice, would elect to see another person in lieu of a physician until he had experienced some satisfactions with the new professional. Thus a consumer must be presented with the program first, almost as a *fait accompli*. In retrospect, we feel that it was naive to expect that many patients, when offered a simple choice between doctor and pharmacist, would opt for the practitioner with less prestige.

In any event the abortive pharmacist-practitioner plan was meant to be a stop-gap measure only. Patients should not have to travel miles to an already over-burdened clinic merely to receive aspirins for a headache or cough syrup for a cold. These problems should be handled on a local level. Ideally we had hoped to develop a new physician's assistant to handle such problems.

A proposal was developed to train a prototypic set of three high school graduates, tentatively called Navameds, as physicians' assistants. While they were to begin their duties in the outpatient department, it was planned that eventually they would also work in satellite field stations treating problems within their areas of competence and referring the rest. Since they would be fluent in both Navajo and English, the communication barrier would be automatically lifted and supportive personnel would be freed. In developing the proposal we worked closely with a neighboring Regional Medical Program but unfortunately a source of funds to support the pilot project could not be located when enthusiasm was high.*

Physician's assistants still strike us as an effective answer to the manpower problem. The solution appeals especially because it simultaneously removes some other barriers to a workable medical system, particularly differences in language, culture, and historical experience between the consumer and the provider. In raising objections to the proposal, or any similar proposals, physicans are wont to claim either that people will not accept nonphysician practitioners or that the patients "deserve better." The first objection seems to contain an element of wishful thinking, since experiences in other settings have shown that consumers can derive great satisfaction in dealing with well-qualified physician assistants. The second pious sentiment is a little hollow. How can one continue talking about patients deserving the very best and then go on giving them something closer to the very worst?

Nor can one blithely assume a deterioration in the quality of care rendered by new health professionals. Preliminary reports on evaluation of their treatments are glowing. Most importantly, these practitioners are more receptive than physicians to the establishment and utilization of standardized methods of diagnosis and treatment. Therefore their performance may be expected to be more consistent than that of the doctor.

In another vein, we sought relief for the nursing personnel. Previous administrations had shied away from the thought of volunteers working within the hospital. The feeling was that the administrative impediments were just

---

* Recently, Indian Health Service programs for training indigenous physicians' assistants have been established in the Navajo and Phoenix Areas. Both of these programs are based in the respective Area medical centers.

too great. But a need existed for people who might offer the patients more of the amenities of life. Eventually the staff was won over to accept the offer of the Hospital Employees Wives' Association to provide the womanpower. The director of nursing became enthusiastic and went to great trouble over setting up the initial arrangements. The club, now considered a hospital auxiliary and open to wider membership, was eagerly responsive. A regular schedule was organized for the volunteers; efforts were concentrated in play therapy for the children and attentions to the elderly. The volunteers attended faithfully and worked diligently.

Reactions were not long in coming. Although the patients showed immediate gratitude (the children especially would wait impatiently for the arrival of the "play ladies") word filtered back from the community that people resented the doctors giving jobs to their wives and depriving the Navajos of employment. The concept of volunteer work was apparently alien to many of the Navajos and could not be understood. Others realized that no payment was involved but still felt that the volunteers were stemming the tide against the day when more Navajo employees would by hired. Naturally when the volunteers learned of the reactions, they withdrew and the program was temporarily abandoned.* The women continued to raise money for the hospital, but stayed out of sight.

We had more success with another endeavor to enlarge our manpower pool. In response to some general inquiries from the University of Utah College of Nursing, we entered into an arrangement to provide increased obstetrical care through the services of nurse-midwives. A project grant application was collaboratively developed and submitted to the National Center for Family Planning. The project featured an intensive family planning program by the midwives based on personalized and comprehensive maternity care. The project was approved and has been funded. In the meantime the midwives have begun to provide obstetrical services and to develop a training program for nurse-midwifery students.

The problems of the curative services may be urgent and dramatic, but the Service Unit also contains an Environmental Health Department with important responsibilities that receive less fanfare. This department had potential to be integrated into the total effort but generally tended to be isolated because of the pressures on the clinical groups.

A discussion with a group of sanitarians about the dearth of evidence

---

* We have been informed by the president of the hospital auxiliary that the volunteer program has been resumed and seems to be well accepted at present.

relating health to living conditions prompted action. The Service Unit's senior sanitarian became inspired to collaborate on a study of housing conditions among a hospitalized group and a control group. The findings showed surprisingly few differences between the two groups.

More important than the actual findings were the indirect results of the study. Environmental health workers began to envisage a new role for themselves in a medical care system. Copies of the report on each family were sent to the doctor in charge of the patient for use in discharge planning. Field health and social service staff began to plan for a collaborative and comprehensive assessment of the home situation (including a sanitarian's evaluation of the environment) as part of the predischarge planning for selected high-risk patients.

One of the prime objectives of the Service Unit must be to provide service. To achieve this, a genuine unit is required, not a conglomeration of parts. The job description of the Service Unit director calls for the unification of all the elements in the organization. The duties include:

> Is responsible for managing, directing, and coordinating the overall operation of the Service Unit, including both medical and nonmedical functional service areas. To establish a continuous cooperative system for individual and group participation with the tribes in the Service Unit for planning, implementing, and evaluating the health programs and policies.

The challenge is great! To achieve the management, direction, and coordination one must find ways to encourage all staff to look beyond their present functioning. Perhaps one of the simplest and most underrated means to this end is the recognition of a job well done. At the Service Unit level where the capacity to reward is rather limited, a word of praise or thanks becomes an important tool. Few people are unaffected by appreciation, especially when it comes from someone in authority or a person whom they respect.

Some workers respond to the opportunity to function at their fullest professional level or to be innovative in their own field. The challenge of seeking a new role for one's profession can be exciting. Others respond to the likelihood of national recognition through presentation of findings at professional meetings or in journals.

Ideally the system should have a reward mechanism built in. Attendance at meetings or special trips should be used as a recognition for service achievement. Unfortunately, in an organization so underfunded there are few goodies to pass out and these fall to the more senior people. We have already noted that promotions are a recognition of longevity more than service and that innovation can be more threatening than helpful to one's career in the Indian Health Service.

Along with recognition of good performance must come an opportunity for responsibility and authority. It is all too easy to become impatient with staff who are slow to respond and to take over oneself. Such centralization is not only inefficient; it fails to develop staff and involve them in change. Particularly in a situation where the turnover is high, a program built around one individual has little chance of permanence unless the staff accept and support it. To paraphrase a VISTA motto, "If they aren't part of the solution, they are part of the problem."

Perhaps our list of the programs and plans generated during one year in Shiprock seems unrealistically long. We recognize that we are describing an organization which was developing new approaches in each department and each discipline. But the abundance of new departures should not surprise anyone. Once an atmosphere receptive to experimentation is achieved, ideas seem to multiply faster than they can be put into practice. The hardest task is to bring about the mood in which change flourishes.

REFERENCES

1. Weed, L. *Medical records, medical education and patient care.* Cleveland: Case Western Reserve University Press, 1969.
2. Lewis, C. F. & Resnick, B. A. Nurse clinics and progressive ambulatory patient care. *New England J. of Medicine,* 1967, *277,* 1236-41.
3. Silver, H. K. *et al.* The pediatric nurse-practitioner program. *J. of American Med. Assoc.,* 1968, *204,* 298-302.
4. Smith, R. A. Medex. *J. of American Med. Assoc.,* 1970, *211,* 1843-45.

Chapter VIII

The Area Office — Is It Necessary?

Many of the problems which daily vex the Indian Health Service cannot be solved at the Service Unit level. Programs, policies, funding, and philosophy depend in a large measure on the bureaucratic superstructure of the Area and the headquarters staffs.

The Area office exists to support the Service Units. One of its major functions is to serve as a middleman between the Service Units and Washington headquarters. In this role the Area is an advocate for the Service Units, an apologist for headquarters, and an arbitrator of conflicting claims between the various Service Units in its jurisdiction. The rationale is that headquarters cannot deal individually with numerous small units and that the service groups cannot spare time and personnel to deal with Washington. The argument is logical and in keeping with modern organizational trends. But in its role as middleman, admittedly a schizophrenic position, the Area office is apt to serve neither headquarters nor the Service Units very well.

The second rationale for the Area office concerns the economic use of personnel and resources. The Area mechanism permits sharing experts among Service Units. The concentration of skills and equipment at the Area level theoretically renders the Area a repository of wisdom for the individual units to tap. Thus the Area staff should be able to facilitate projects by offering advice and consultation on technical and professional issues as well as on the logistics of working within the Indian Health Service hierarchy.

Finally, the Area provides a system for communication and cross-fertilization among Service Units which, at least in theory, have similar problems. The Area is able to strive for uniform standards of service and to juggle assignments of personnel to this end. In addition to its other functions, then, the Area might also be able to exercise quality control within its jurisdiction.

In practice, how does the system work? Unfortunately, promotion by attrition takes its toll, so that Area personnel are not always equipped

91

intellectually for their leadership positions. Consultations with Area specialists generally become platitudinous pep-talks, somehow irrelevant to the immediate problems of the firing lines. In the higher echelons, a sense of identification with and compassion for the man at the bottom is often lacking—yet this ingredient is the essence of dynamic leadership.

The high turnover at the Service Unit level is one of the strong arguments for a vigorous Area office which can ensure continuity of programs. While the Area is relatively free of conflict betwen careerists and two-year men, its homogeneity brings other problems. For many careerists, the Area is a calm Sargasso Sea removed from both the storms of the Service Unit and the currents of politicking and policy-making at the Washington headquarters. Area staff many find the becalmed state relaxing, but the situation is agonizingly frustrating for those who want to move messages between headquarters and the Service Units.

As a buffer between headquarters and the Service Units, the Area personnel are caught among conflicting pressures. They must provide innumerable pieces of data for compilation into service-wide reports required by headquarters, yet they are besieged by demands for assistance in local problem-solving. The Area presses the needs of the Service Units in Washington and then explains the policies which filter back.

Perhaps more than anything else, the Area acts as a clearing house, forwarding information on to the appropriate (or the inappropriate) point at headquarters. As a former Service Unit director, it is hard for me to recall an instance when the Area dealt with a question directly. The instinctive reflex seems to be to reach for the telephone and check with a superior authority.

The inability to assume responsibility is matched by a failure to delegate it. One creative Service Unit director in a small facility had arranged for the Army Corps of Engineers to build an addition onto his hospital. The Area nearly delayed the project into extinction after it established control over the operation. While Area experts studied the question, they were wasting the time when the army personnel was available to begin construction. Similarly, in our own Service Unit, the grant application for the family planning program written with the University of Utah College of Nursing was nearly sabotaged because the Area was reluctant to approve the program and guarantee interim support. At stake was a million dollar program—virtually a gift to the greater prestige of the Navajo Area—but the Area office showed no urgency in accepting it.

The Area offices cannot be by-passed. A Service Unit director on one of the Great Plains reservations worked with his constituents and the local BIA officials to develop jointly a multiple service center. The center was to include a mental health clinic, offices for CHR's, an alcohol treatment center, a juvenile home, and a community jail. Funding was to come in part from BIA allocations for the jail and from a contribution from the tribe. The Service Unit director approached the regional director of HEW for any assistance he could provide, including the possibility of making available an unused portion of a local Veteran's Administration hospital for a regional Indian alcoholism treatment center.

This enterprising Service Unit director was rebuffed. He received no help from HEW, but was chastised by the Indian Health Service for writing directly to the regional director without clearing or communicating through his Area office.

A favorite Area device is inaction. The Area may insist on assuming control of a situation and then, by doing nothing, preserve the *status quo*. The Service Unit is then impotent to develop plans to attack the problem or even to institute communications on the issue. The smoldering problem either extinguishes itself, or occasionally, erupts into a major brushfire. The same group who advocates a preventive approach to disease insists on delayed treatment for administrative ailments.

An example of the stalling technique occurred in Shiprock. The Service Unit director was subpoenaed to appear before a county grand jury to account for his policies in spending contract medical funds in the off-reservation city hospital. Welcoming the opportunity to air the issue, he prepared a detailed documentation of the reasons for his priorities. The Area office gave its blessing but several hours before the hearing nervously changed course. Since the matter of contract medical funds had "Area-wide implications," the Area personnel decided to take over the testimony. The first step of the new spokesmen was to request more time to document the issue. A postponement was granted and the matter dropped completely.

A similar situation arose when a local missionary establishment announced that it could no longer provide physician services to its several thousand Navajo patients. The Service Unit met with the mission staff to consider alternative solutions. The mission felt that clinical care could be maintained by nurse practitioners without a reduction in quality if Indian Health Service doctors could provide coverage on a weekly basis. Since such a decision was a matter of policy, the Area was consulted. Rejecting the local plan, the Area volunteered to help recruit a replacement physician. The mission clinic closed for lack of coverage and will likely remain inoperative until consumer demands force PHS action.

The atmosphere around the Area office (which also pervades bureaucrats at all levels) is one of anxious concern over the whims of Congress. The dependency on Congressional allocations is undeniable, but does not justify the enormous quantities of emotional energy which are devoted to divining the mysterious intent of this cornucopia. Omens are cited, soothsayers consulted, rumors and gossip analyzed. Area personnel visit the Service Units and reassure them when the mood of Congress appears favorable. Not only is this preoccupation time-wasting, but it also provides a perfect scapegoat for the Area offices.

Clearly, lump sum Congressional funding has resulted in inappropriate or disproportionate support of Indian Health programs at times. Each year the budget requests are trimmed to skeletal dimensions. Certain areas of spending attract Congressional sponsorship more readily than others; of course, novelty is more enticing to legislators than necessity.

Funds are committed to specific programs with more largesse than they are allocated to maintenance of ongoing activities. It is more satisfying to a congressman to vote a large sum of money to eliminate a disease entity than to support mundane and unglamorous everyday programs which will reappear annually. It is inconsequential that the disease may be less threatening to the Indian population than some of the less exotic killers and cripplers. Perhaps that is why it is easier to get money for trachoma than for eyeglasses.

Each year the discrepancy widens between the needs of patient care programs and their budgets. Routine care is not exciting but it is vital. While part of the system talks about comprehensive health care, another part makes minimal acute care almost impossible.

The whim of Congress readily becomes the whipping boy for the failure to initiate successful programs. More positive approaches are available. While the Indian Health Service, as a federal agency, is ineligible to receive grant money from another federal agency, it is possible to gain access to such funds to support demonstration and pilot projects. The key lies in affiliation. Working with a variety of organizations such as medical schools, regional medical programs, or even tribes, the Indian Health Service can obtain funds for which these groups are the designated recipients. The Family Planning Project in Shiprock is such an example; in this case the impetus for affiliation came from the Service Unit level.

Collaboration with universities offers more than an economic advantage. If the Area offices deliberately enter into partnership with educational institutions, a new image is developed for the Indian Health Service. Students are brought into contact with a dynamic agency which may appear attractive as a future employer. The Indian Health Service gains wider exposure for its programs and staffing needs. Consultations spill over into areas of Indian health not directly related to the demonstration project.

Over the years the Navajo Area has worked with universities in several capacities. Despite the potential, these associations have failed to have great impact.

In the early days of the PHS's work with the Indians, contracts were let out with two schools of public health and a medical school to study specific problems in health care and to develop programs in these respective areas.

Cornell Medical School studied the problem of tuberculosis control. After initial hospital-based work in antituberculosis chemotherapy, the researchers moved out into the community. Their demonstration project in the region of Many Farms, Arizona, is well described by Adair and Deuschle in *The People's Health* (1). The Cornell team was able to demonstrate the great usefulness of a local health worker, dubbed "health visitor," who was trained to carry out many vital tasks including interpretation, home visiting, and health education. With the termination of the project, its practical impact evaporated rapidly. Despite the proven effectiveness of native, locally trained paramedicals, no further use or experimentation was made with this kind of worker until very recently.

The University of California School of Public Health established a field station in the western part of the Navajo reservation near Tuba City, Arizona. This group focused on problems in health education and communication. Although any number of anthropological monographs were written on the need for understanding the culture, again little practical impact was felt. Instruction manuals, guidelines, curricula, and project reports emphasized the crucial role of the interpreter in reservation health care, but to this day nobody is employed in the Navajo Area as an interpreter. (Only in the past year has interpreting even been recognized by the Indian Health Service as a job description and a basis for a wage scale.)

A durable association was developed with the University of North Carolina School of Public Health, which undertook to develop a training program for health educators. Although no specific innovations or institutions can be noted as a result of the training activities, the North Carolina courses constitute the bulk of instruction of health educators currently employed on the Navajo reservation.

Informal affiliations with medical schools have evolved over the years. For some time medical students from the Department of Preventive Medicine of the University of Pittsburg School of Medicine have been sponsored in preceptorships at Fort Defiance. Medical students from Yale have worked in various locations across the reservation for the past two summers. Less regular arrangements exist between various schools and individual Service Units, as well as formal assignments for students in the health professions through the Commissioned Officer Student Training and Extern Program (COSTEP). Occasionally housestaff from nearby medical centers have rotated through Indian Health Service assignments to gain clinical experience while augmenting manpower.

The university influence has not had the effect one might have hoped. It has not brought about a widespread questioning of basic policies and a challenge of dogma. And yet the need is growing to examine activities and establish priorities for the expenditure of scarce resources.

One of the Area functions which we have mentioned is that of drawing together the Service Unit leaders for common planning on mutual problems. Every six weeks or so in the Navajo Area the Service Unit directors met together along with officials from the Area office. In 1969, the Service Unit directors decided to look for a rational and concerted approach to the problem of the Contract Medical Care (or CMC) fund.

In addition to providing direct health care and public health services to its beneficiaries, the Indian Health Service also acts as third-party sponsor for medical care. The Indian Health Service purchases outside medical care when services can be provided more economically by this method, or when services are required which are not available at the regular PHS installations. The latter include emergency care, when the health of the patient might be jeopardized by transfer to a PHS hospital, and specialized care, such as heart surgery, neurosurgery, or radiation therapy.

Each Service Unit is allocated an ear-marked sum for such contract medical care expenses, and this is the CMC fund. The supply of money does not usually meet the demand. The funds are allocated on a loose historical basis (the more you spend this year, the more you are likely to get next year) in fiscal quarters. This method of budgeting leads to inequitable outcomes. A patient with an illness requiring specialized treatment might be referred for care at one point in time and not at another, depending on the solvency of the CMC account. Early in the fiscal year a patient might be denied specialty treatment for fear of insolvency. Yet in the waning months any potential surplus would be expended on similar patients (or even those less ill) to prevent subsequent reduction of the allocation.

Habitually, the CMC funds have gone first to provide acute medical care. The remainder has been used for care of more chronic problems such as corrective ear surgery for children with severe hearing impairments or open-heart surgery for congenital heart disease. In reality, little money is usually left for funding the chronic problems, even those which yield well to treatment.

The Service Unit directors in the Navajo Area discussed this problem and decided to attack the issue in concert. Recommendations were made to render the CMC policies and regulations more uniform across the Navajo Area. Agreements on procedures were reached rather quickly, but eventually became bogged down in the molasses of Area implementation.

The Service Unit directors also initiated a project to develop a method of assigning priorities for the use of CMC funds. The plan was quite involved and required sustained interest on the part of the group. Unfortunately, although initial enthusiasm was high among the SUD's, their interest in such a collaborative endeavor was subverted by a reversion to individual concerns over the effects on their own Service Units.

The description of this priority-setting project is detailed as an example of one approach to meeting the growing problem of medical decision-making. Despite our position as the most affluent nation on earth, we are gradually recognizing our inability to be all things to all people. It does not appear feasible to provide every citizen with the full range of medical care achievements currently available. Some system of priorities will evolve. It may be haphazard distribution based on ability to pay or it can be a rationally planned effort based on the knowledge of the benefit to be expected for the cost.

From the inspiration of work by Dr. John Williamson and others at Johns Hopkins School of Public Health in a field he calls "prognostic epidemiology," we sought to develop a rational method for allocating priorities for CMC dollars. The overall assumption was that funds should go to treat those conditions for which treatment would yield the greatest result for the investment.

Yield was defined as the difference in outcome between the natural course of the untreated disease and the results of skilled medical intervention. This difference can be measured in terms of time (survival), function, comfort, or economic productivity. Because of widespread unemployment among the Navajo, it seemed inappropriate to develop the economic component; most Navajos, however able-bodied, could not find jobs. Our emphasis was placed on time, function, and comfort.

Data on the natural course of most diseases is relatively scarce. Information on how treatment affects the patient in terms of increasing his comfort and restoring his function is practically nonexistent. We therefore had to rely on the best clinical judgment of physicians who had experience treating Navajos. Arbitrarily we established five levels of function (from "confined to bed" through "up and about") and five levels of pain and discomfort (from "extreme pain and discomfort" through "no discomfort, feels well"). Each of these levels from the treated and untreated states contained a time element to allow for the effect of the fatal outcome of a disease and the age of the patient. The products of the weighted levels times the time factor were to be summed, resulting in an overall score for both the treated and the untreated states. The difference between these scores was to be divided by the average cost of specialty care.*

An obvious example of the rationale behind this construct is the discrepancy between the cost yield ratio for an emergency operation to extract a peanut from the windpipe of a two-year-old and a lengthy series of x-ray treatments for a 65-year-old man with inoperable lung cancer. Immediately one perceives that the former procedure is quite inexpensive and yet, by one dramatic intervention, ensures the patient of a whole life-time of normal functioning with no pain or discomfort. The contrast with the elderly terminal cancer patient is obvious. However, in many instances, the issues are not as clearcut and a tool, such as the formula described here, can help the administration sort them out.

Although this approach to priority setting seems reminiscent of earlier PHS misadventures with the Q-formula, certain differences should be noted. This was not an attempt to establish priorities for a total comprehensive health approach; it was a tool for dealing with curative situations which already had presented themselves. Frequency of occurrence and ease of detection or prevention are not relevant in this instance. We recognized that

---

* The overall formula can be expressed as:

$$\text{Yield} = \frac{\left[\sum(C_{1\text{-}5} \cdot T_c) + \sum(F_{1\text{-}5} \cdot T_f)\right] \text{Tr} - \left[\sum(C_{1\text{-}5} \cdot T_c) + \sum(F_{1\text{-}5} \cdot T_f)\right] \overline{\text{Tr}}}{Co_\$}$$

C	=	Comfort score on a 1-5 scale
T_c	=	Time of each level of comfort noted
F	=	Function score on a 1-5 scale
T_f	=	Time of each level of function noted
$Co_\$$	=	Average cost of care in dollars
Tr	=	Treated
$\overline{\text{Tr}}$	=	Untreated

the data behind the formula was based on "guesstimates" and did not try to utilize inappropriate or inaccurate statistics.

To test the concept we solicited the aid of approximately 20 physicians who were recommended as extensively experienced with clinical medicine on the Navajo reservation. Each physician was mailed a questionnaire which explained the project and asked him to complete his estimates for four conditions: chronic otitis media with hearing loss, the common cold, normal obstetrical delivery, and acute subdural hematoma.

Six physicians responded with varying levels of completeness. The responses (and the nonresponses) seemed to indicate great reluctance, if not outright resistance, to approach the problem in this way. Even those who completed the questionnaire expressed grave uncertainty about the use of estimates or the rationale behind the project. In the words of one respondent, "Any answer would represent a guess with absolutely no validity. If you plan to use the responses for judging something else, I would say you are building on sand."

Throughout the entire experiment the Area personnel played a role no more active than mute observation. The indifference of the Area and the lack of support from clinicians was sufficient to curtail any further effort toward so mathematical an approach. Nevertheless, a philosophy of cost benefit was enacted by the SUD's. A list of priorities was developed that discouraged the use of CMC funds for the treatment of conditions such as chronic renal disease, end-stage cancer, severe burns, and spinal cord injuries. At the same time corrective ear surgery and heart surgery were given more precedence in the CMC priority list.

Perhaps, considering its negligible practical effect, we have described this abortive effort at systemization in monotonous detail. Yet the project did represent an effort for all the Service Units on the reservation to work together and to attack a mutual problem as logically as possible. And discussions of the problem at the regular SUD meetings was a welcome respite on an agenda which formerly seemed devoted to analysis of the "mood of Congress."

The Area's approach to CMC funding still remained the spend-when-you-can, save-when-you-have-to, and hunt-for-extra-funds system. Several years ago, the Area's leadership was well illustrated by its dealings with one Navajo Service Unit which presented high CMC bills. The spending went on unchecked until a memo arrived stating that no further authorizations of CMC funds would be permitted for the remainder of the fiscal year. Any physician authorizing such care was warned that he would be held personally liable for the costs and billed accordingly. The Service Unit medical staff responded immediately and furiously with a counter-ultimatum threatening to curtail all clinic services in such an event. From previously untapped sources, Area funds were quickly produced to support CMC care for the duration of the year. The Area had tried to flex its muscle and had achieved only a charley-horse.

We recognize the real problems faced by the Area office in its effort to provide services and staff across the vast reservation region. This task must be accomplished with tight funds and policies that are often dictated from above. Yet even within these limitations, the Area office possibly could stimulate and encourage local efforts.

Encouragement and stimulation are the commodities most lacking when the Area meets the Service Unit. We keep reverting to the theme of appreciation because we believe that simple recognition of the efforts of others could do much to revitalize the whole Indian Health Service. Again we could illustrate from the Shiprock Service Unit during our tenure. Expecting a delegation from the Area, including the Area director, the medical staff prepared a detailed presentation of the needs of the Service Unit and plans for future programs. They gathered and analyzed data to demonstrate their needs and justify their proposals. The physicians were eager to learn how the Area responded to their departures in procedure and to accept help with the problems presented.

When a reaction came, it was more dampening than criticism. A memo from the Area director was circulated to all Service Units noting that the Area director was generally pleased with his observations during his recent tour of the Service Units. The communication went on to state that he was concerned, however, to notice a general laxity in the wearing of uniforms. Specific instances were cited. Since the Shiprock Service Unit received no individualized response to its presentation, the physicians resented the uniform memo fiercely. Months later we had an opportunity to discuss this reaction with the Area personnel and they, in turn, were perplexed. What did the officers expect? The Area director claimed that if he were to send around memos commending people, he would be dictating memos all day. Yet any effort to appeal to a step higher in the hierarchy leads to more bewilderment in the Area office. The plaintive, but sincere, question is heard, "Why don't they feel they can come to us with their problems?"

We would put the question differently. Why does anyone have to come to the Area with a problem? Is the Area mechanism necessary?

We have observed that the Area office tends to be an unsatisfactory middleman—cautious, indecisive, and procrastinating. As an expert consultant, the Area has failed to inspire. The Area has been a focus for planning efforts with outside agencies, in particular the university, but we have noted that recommendations from university-sponsored studies have failed to work. Perhaps the university effort would be more effective if infused through the lower echelons, or if real decision-making was possible on a lower level. Finally, the Area has not exercised leadership in bringing the Service Units together for common problem-solving; activities of this nature have gone on in spite of Area indifference.

Our own observations in the Navajo Area showed the Area office doing as much hindering as facilitating. Yet this criticism alone is not reason for abolishing the department. Changes could be made which would render the Area office a true leader with the power to advise and stimulate the Service Units. The intriguing alternative, however, would be to disband the Area office and divide its funds and staff among the Service Units in the jurisdiction.

The result could be an invitation to chaos, with dozens of groups trying to get the attention of headquarters. But the change could also be invigorating. Each Service Unit would be forced to do its own headcounting in as meaningful a way as possible, for each unit would have much more of a stake in its statistics. Presumably each Service Unit would need to retain an employee who would act as a lobbyist in Washington. This would be no more taxing, however, than formerly, when the Service Unit's personnel spent hours communicating with the Area office. From the viewpoint of headquarters, the situation might be a little more confusing, but conceivably Washington could appoint a dozen men to act as liaisons with a group of Service Units at much less expense than staffing an Area office.

If each Service Unit presented its own budget and programs, each would be able to deal directly with the consumers of medical care in a more meaningful way. The patients could join with the administration in attempts to persuade headquarters and/or Congress of their Unit's particular needs.

If personnel presently at the Area were dispersed and future Service Units handled their own staffing, the various Service Units would develop particular strengths and characteristics. The interests, aptitudes, and training of the personnel would shape the sort of programs developed. In this hypothetical situation, one could imagine one Service Unit developing a mental health bias and another emphasizing environmental measures. Perhaps some units would concentrate on inpatient care while others would develop a network of clinics more fully. Uniformity would suffer, but perhaps excellence might appear here and there. And excellence is a quality which is scarce throughout the Indian Health Service.

Without the Area office, communication between Service Units would still be possible. As certain regions developed a reputation for particular skills, they might have opportunities to instruct others. Consultations could move horizontally between Service Units instead of vertically between the Area and its Service Units.

Abolition of the Area structure is a drastic solution and, of course, not likely to be implemented. But the speculation is suggestive for new health organizations which may be federally-funded. We are not really sure how much administrative apparatus can be placed on top of a service program without smothering that program's spirit.

The most cogent reason for retaining the Area office is the need for continuity because of the high turnover of personnel in the Service Units. But perhaps the present hierarchical structure exacerbates this very problem. Under a revised system probably careerists would be appointed to positions of power within the Service Units and would not be shuttled away to a central office. The local turnover would then not be as great and automatically the continuity would be better.

This exercise in imagining the Area away is worthwhile if just to give proper perspective to our bureaucratic organizations. The agency framework must exist to serve the overall goals of the operation. Any department can test its relevance by imagining the organization without it. In the case of the Area offices of the Indian Health Service, such a test should send the personnel scurrying to their desks to start working on internal reform.

REFERENCE

1. Adair, J. & Deuschle, K. *The people's health.* New York: Appleton-Century-Crofts, 1970.

Chapter IX
Searching Again — Practice-Oriented Research

In the public imagination, research conjures up images of test-tubes and white-coated scientists in sterile laboratories. Even to many within the medical professions, research is often identified with years of painstaking labor under carefully controlled conditions. A certain mystique about doing research deters many from beginning. A fear of unreachable exactitudes or frustratingly unproductive experimentation leads many health practitioners to abandon research to the experts.

Yet research need not be so formidable. The word itself implies "looking again," a fresh examination of problems (and solutions) that have gone stale. As such, it can be a potent managerial tool to encourage staff to rethink a question or re-examine an activity that has become routinized.

Too often medical research is reserved for larger centers where sophisticated equipment is available: the research grants transfuse new blood into the center's anemic finances. This tendency to relegate research to specialized institutions has been extended to clinical, epidemiologic, and health services research. Artificial models are created and tested in place of real-life situations. Certainly it is an advantage for the investigator to be able to manipulate the variables, but the prototype is tainted with the other-worldliness of the university. If we are to make headway in solving practical problems, we must also encourage research in the world of actual practice, ideally in collaboration with the expertise of the university.

The newly established National Center for Health Services Research and Development has recognized this need and its implications for the potential creation of on-going models. It seeks to fund community organizations which can then contract with universities for expert consultation. Local community groups are more likely to develop programs which will continue after the fervor of experimentation has subsided.

The Indian Health Service has developed its own health services research center. The Health Programs System Center (HPSC) is located on the San

103

Xavier Indian Reservation among the Papago tribe near Tucson, Arizona. The mission of the organization is reiterated in the preface to each of its reports:

> ... to develop, test, refine and demonstrate optimal ways of planning, budgeting, implementing and evaluating the [Indian Health Service] comprehensive program of community health services. ... Diversified operations reseach and system-analysis methods are being utilized to develop more objective descriptions of health problems and priorities; to the development of responsive health information systems; to health service models and simulations; to allocation methods for maximizing available resources; to efficient utilization of professional and auxiliary manpower; and to meaningful planning and evaluation methods.

This is a very impressive list. Any one of the objectives, if realized, would be a substantial contribution to the national health care scene. Unfortunately, few meaningful contributions have been felt in the Indian Health Service at large. At HPSC substantial work has been completed on a computerized health information system which could unify health records, but the system is not developed beyond similar efforts elsewhere. A variety of reports and studies have swelled the literature on subjects ranging from a simulation model for T.B. control to a time study of outpatient visits or the relationship of trachoma to environmental sanitation. These projects, however, have had little effect on practices outside the rarified atmosphere of the center.

Unfortunately, many share the attitude of a PHS employee who was asked what changes could be made in present Indian Health Service's activities which would most improve the people's health. This employee, who identified himself as a white, college-educated man with over ten years in the Public Health Service and a major role in planning, was reluctant to commit himself:

> HPSC is presently working on various plans to provide current statistics on patients being treated in more than one service unit, rechannelling the efforts of Public Health Nurses, etc. There are other changes I might suggest, but without research would not necessarily be valid. I would leave this to the experts now working on the problems.

Employees are generally willing to "leave it to the experts." But the most sophisticated studies conducted at a distance by experts will not necessarily convince local practitioners that their behavior needs altering. An escape-hatch is available for, after all, the experts may not be aware of local extenuating conditions. The study results, they say, do not really apply to every Service Unit. For example, it is unlikely that the most carefully documented study emanating from HPSC would have convinced the Shiprock public health nurses that much of their expensive time was being wasted. Yet the simple exercise (hardly complicated enough to be dignified with the label "research") of counting uncompleted home visits and minutes spent in travelling and paper work brought this fact home in an indisputable way. Faced with evidence they had collected themselves, the nurses were more willing than before to consider a change in the structure of their department.

This credibility factor is aggravated by the inaccessibility of HPSC. Consultation services from HPSC staff are difficult to obtain for Service Unit problems. The Center's specialists share the reluctance of their colleagues to work in the real world. The conflict between practitioners and researchers found in the civilian arena exists to an even sharper degree in the Indian Health Service, where the providers of care are increasingly resentful of allocations to HPSC which bring them no tangible results, no stimulation, no help.

Nature abhors vacuums, but researchers seem to thrive in them. Evaluations of ongoing programs in an organization as large as the Indian Health Service cannot be limited to one oasis of talent. Every local unit should be encouraged to examine its activities critically, to revise those which are ineffectual, and to strengthen and improve those which are achieving their objectives. Finally, the objectives themselves must constantly be checked for relevance. Such an emphasis is difficult to introduce unilaterally in a Service Unit. Central support is required both for funds to hire experts and, more important, for the administrative flexibility which makes change possible on the basis of local findings.

It would be most imprecise to ignore research which has been carried out by other elements within the Indian Health Service, apart from HPSC. Unfortunately, the bulk of this research deals with clinical studies rather than with new techniques in problem-solving. A bibliography prepared by the United States National Library of Medicine for the years 1964-1968 on "Indian Health in the U.S. and Canada" listed 228 citations. Almost 200 dealt with clinical epidemiologic reports and historical accounts ranging from "Anthropological and psychological observations on Tarahumara endurance runners" to "Roentgenographic evaluation of temporal bones from South

Dakota Indian burials." We requested the bibliography prior to assuming duties on the Navajo reservation, but articles in the vein of the ones cited were obviously of no value in facing up to the health problems of the Service Unit.

On the Navajo reservation itself a variety of problems have been studied and reported, including diabetes, malnutrition, suicides and accidents, congenital hip disease, tuberculosis, and cirrhosis. Regular national conferences are held with groups such as the American Public Health Association and the American Academy of Pediatrics. Task forces are appointed and reports filed. The policy makers use these tools to make their policies, but who makes them work?

Nor have the ethnologists been less prolific. In one bibliography compiled in 1965 by David Bugge of the Navajo Land Claim and Navajo Tribal Museum, over 375 titles are listed, excluding a number of historical and archival sources and with apologies for failing to include all titles dated 1960 or later. The resentment of the Indians at all this study with so little to show for it is well expressed by one Indian, Vine Deloria, in his manifesto *Custer Died for Your Sins.* The various brands of anthropologist-cultural, economic, political and historical-are alike condemned as parasites on Indian societies. Their research consists of verifying preconceived opinions.

Worse yet, according to Vine Deloria, the research of the anthropologists is decidedly dangerous, since it has been the basis for irrelevant government programs.

> Behind each successful man stands a woman, and behind each policy and program with which Indians are plagued, if traced completely back to its origin, stands the anthropologists (1).

Anthropologists' studies resolve themselves into pat slogans such as "caught between two cultures" which serve to obscure the need for any constructive programs to eliminate poverty, disease, and hunger, or to redress legal wrongs. Moreover the anthropologists' data comes from a mixture of historical and mythical sources until it takes on a monumental irrelevance to practical concerns. Again in the words of Deloria:

> Would they [the Irish] submit to a group of Indians coming to Boston and telling them what a modern Irishman was like? Expecting them to dress in green and hunt leprechauns so as to live on the leprechaun's hidden gold would hardly provide a meaningful path to the future (2).

So it is with some trepidation that we urge all health professionals to become research-minded. We do not advocate that medical students come to the reservations and become instant analysts of the Indian cultures and their relationship to health. We would wish for students of the health system to avoid the pitfalls of convenient cultural explanations. "Caught between two medical cultures" is another slogan which can cover a multitude of poor programs and conveniently ignore factors such as poverty, inaccessibility, and lack of medical resources when explaining low levels of health. And, above all, the research which exists in a practical vacuum must be avoided if any sort of rapport is to exist between the Indians and their medical purveyors. The Indians are tired of being under the microscope.

Rather than put the Indian cultures under the microscope, we suggest a microscopic scrutiny of the health care system.

Research can be meaningful and productive when it is incorporated into the ongoing activities of a Service Unit. If the research is to take time and effort away from service demands, it must be relevant to the problems faced on the medical firing lines. Personnel is in short supply, so it will be difficult to break the vicious cycle in which the employee is too busy, albeit inefficiently or ineffectively, to examine what he is doing.

Other sources of manpower can be identified to assist in the ongoing research process. Medical students can perform a very valuable function in this respect. When a medical student assigned to a Service Unit conducts a study, Indian Health Service personnel are involved in the planning and day-to-day conduct of the inquiry in a way which is impossible when the research is handled by the remote HPSC. The permanent personnel are freed from much of the leg-work but are spared none of the important headwork. It is a truism but true that the person who sets out seriously to teach must learn in the process.

The role of students in an isolated setting such as the Service Unit could be recognized and exploited. To some skeptics, the student looms as an added burden on the time and attention of staff, yet we have found that the student, regardless of his discipline, gives far more than he gets. The relationship is not exploitive—any student realizes that he gains more from experiences which allow him to make a contribution. If a student's role is genuinely productive, the advantage of all parties is served.

At various times during our year in Shiprock, the Service Unit worked with students in medicine, nursing, dentistry, hospital administration, laboratory, environmental health, and social work. The benefits of the connection depended on whether the department troubled to offer adequate supervision and integrate the student into its regular functions. In any department the student can be an unbiased observer who should be encouraged to question what he sees. Students bring the Service Units closer to the university and the consultation it can offer. The university also may provide computer services and specialized tests. Most of all, university connections should be a source of stimulation, a challenge to rethink old ideas and come up with new solutions.

Students do represent manpower, particularly for tasks which may not conform to the staff's concept of its role. Students also can go places and ask questions which might not be tolerated in a professional. The student is not identified with the health establishment in a way which prejudices the result of opinion surveys. A medical student from far-away New York City was able to elicit frank responses in a poll of PHS employees—a regular staff member could not expect to do the same.

The staff study, reported in a previous chapter, was the work of a fourth-year medical student from Mt. Sinai School of Medicine, now Dr. John Jacoby, who spent about three months of his final year in Shiprock. During that time he worked out the design of the research, conducted the interviews and analyzed the data. He consulted with local advisors, ensuring that his choice of subject would interest Service Unit personnel. Dr. Jacoby's work was ambitious for a student project and yet was manageable within the time period. He himself found the study gratifying and is considering a career in the health planning field.

The consumer study which was described earlier was also partially the work of a medical student from Case Western Reserve.* He prepared the questionnaire and worked on the coding instrument while the actual interviews were conducted by the CHR's in the Navajo language. Student activities also prompted the fresh examination of the field health program. Two students from Yale Medical School observed the Department of Field Health during six weeks in the summer. Their supervisors were clinicians who encouraged their proteges to find ammunition to attack what they considered an unproductive and expensive department. The students obliged, but in so doing set the machinery in motion which subsequently stimulated the director of Field Health to do her own examination of the data and to work out practical solutions.

Simple research projects have tested clinical impressions. The pediatri-

* This student's reactions to his Shiprock experience are embodied in an article: Peter Rudd, "Navajo Health Care: A Case for Priorities," *Case Western Reserve Medical Alumni Bulletin*, 1970. *XXXIV*, 4-6.

cians, for example, were continuously remarking that cases of child neglect or failure to thrive seemed to be associated with families in which the mother worked at the local industry. Public statements in the national press had also suggested that this industrialization was probably responsible for child neglect. When a medical student expressed an interest in studying maternal and child health problems, a simple but effective retrospective study was designed. Her work showed that rates of neglected children were no higher among employed mothers than among the control group.

Student projects may point out deficiencies in our own data. One student was interested in gathering data on the numerous highway accidents in the Service Unit. He was assured by both state and tribal police that large stores of information were immediately available. After designing a study instrument and requesting his data from the police, he was unable to get any information for several months. Slowly it became apparent that, while a great amount of information was recorded about each accident, little of the information was accessible.

All research does not need to be sponsored by students. In the preceding chapters of this book we have alluded to other research projects. The auditing of medical records was designed as a study with a built-in evaluation procedure. The sanitation department has been involved in a field study of the relationship between environmental conditions and disease. The obstetrician became actively engaged in the planning of the midwife demonstration project which also allows for periodic evaluation. The pharmacy department, as mentioned earlier, even sought special funds from a drug company to support its study of pharmacologic auditing. In each case, once a department became committed to the idea of studying a problem, it became infused with new energy and enthusiasm.

The reaction at the Area level to this research activity was remarkable. Headquarters had recently urged the Indian Health Service to publish more in the medical literature and thus disseminate information about its activities more widely. Area naturally passed on those words of encouragement, yet the Area office seemed to share the old mystique about research, preferring to see it carried out by specialized units from the universities or from HPSC. Despite a card sorter for analysis of the outpatient data system, most of Area research consisted in preparing statistical reports to answer the needs of others. Occasionally, if coaxed, Area might provide more than numbers of services performed and go on to analyze distribution or deficits.

In regard to one study conducted at Shiprock, indifference gave way to obstructionism. The study of staff attitudes and opinions about the medical care system was originally planned as a Service Unit project. However, as discussions began and interest rose, it seemed appropriate to seek a wider data base and extend the project over the entire Navajo area. We met with the Area director to explain the protocol, the questionnaire, and the proposed analysis of the data. We noted our intention of obtaining consultation from medical school experts on the design and analysis of the instrument. The director indicated his interest and approval, even requesting the addition of a special question on planning.

Halfway through the data collection phase, after the questionnaires were mailed out, we were astonished to receive a memorandum from the director questioning the qualifications of the researchers, our plans for data analysis, and our intentions for the use of the results. The memo challenged the instrument on a number of points of design, bias, and content—the same instrument which the director had read and approved a few weeks earlier. Copies of the memo were sent to all Service Unit directors and branch chiefs in the Area office.

We received a number of puzzled inquiries from colleagues about this reaction. One branch chief, a two-year man, even wrote the Area director a memo of support for the study. In this officer's rejoinder he explained a fact that the whole Indian Health Service sometimes ignores:

However, it might be recognized that opinions mold health behavior as much as the objective facts of which we are fond.

Eventually the Area was reassured that the research was legitimate and perhaps even worthwhile. The project proceeded, although Area personnel gave the poorest response rate of any geographical region in the survey.

Almost immediately after the incident involving Mr. Jacoby's study, the creation of an Area Research Committee was announced. Its function was to exercise review over all research designs prior to their implementation.

The impediments, both active and passive, which the Area places in the way of local research might tempt Service Unit staffs to abandon its pursuit to the university and the HPSC group. But here we must heed the cautionary words of the Cornell Project Report by Adair and Deuschle. The Cornell Project was a demonstration in tuberculosis control which was conducted by Cornell Medical school under contract from the Public Health Service. This work demonstrated quite conclusively how useful a group of Navajo workers, known as "health visitors" could be. Upon termination of the contract, however, the Public Health Service had no ability to assimilate the health visitors into the system and was unwilling to allow them to work at their previous level of responsibility.

Adair and Deuschle regretfully concluded:

Innovation is not likely to take place by direct diffusion to the middle and lower echelons of government from an outside agency no matter how great the need. The lesson to be learned from the above example is that in the medical field innovations may be more readily accepted by the recipient society... than by the government of the donor society, wherein any change must overcome numerous vested interests of the professions and bureaucratic organization.

Stated in another way, there is a higher level of motivation on the part of the acculturated Navajo to learn from us than we have to learn from him (3).

This is a grim prognosis for the effectiveness of far-off research findings in bringing about local change. On an individual basis, it is comparable to handing the patient a life-saving medicine only to be met with a refusal to swallow. Perhaps the medicine would be more palatable, though no less effective, if it had been concocted by Indian Health Service cooks.

For this reason we hope for increased research and research-mindedness on a Service Unit level. At the same time we would advocate strengthening ties with the universities by all possible means, including the use of students, so that the studies and projects could approach the high level of the Cornell experiment.

REFERENCES

1. Deloria, V. *Custer died for your sins.* New York: Macmillan Co., 1969, p. 81.
2. *Ibid.* pp 92-93.
3. Adair, J. and Deuschle, K. *The people's health.* New York: Appleton-Century-Crofts, 1970, pp. 148-149.

Chapter X
Getting Along with the Neighbors

The medical care system is just one of the many systems which constitute a community. In a rural setting such as Shiprock (and most other Indian Health Service units), the structure of community life can be observed more readily than in urban areas. The various systems within the community are interdependent to some degree. The health agency must react to the activities of other powers in the region, and the health agency has learned to expect quick and sensitive reactions to any of its own internal changes.

We have already made reference to several impinging relationships between the medical system and the tribal political system. The medical and economic fates of the community are also intertwined, both directly in terms of subsidization of medical care and indirectly in terms of the general relationship between socioeconomic level and health status.

In Shiprock itself the Service Unit interacts with a variety of agencies which represent many aspects of community life. The Bureau of Indian Affairs, the longstanding exerciser of power in Indian communities, must collaborate with PHS around several mutual problems.

One of the major functions of the BIA has been and is education. Approximately half of the Navajo children on the reservation are enrolled in BIA boarding schools. (The rest attend public schools which are becoming more common as transportation improves.) When PHS assumed responsibility for the health of the Indians in 1955, agreements were made to provide school health services as part of the total program. Joint policy statements by BIA and PHS officials set out requirements for the school care. The PHS had committed itself to a program it could not meet and the BIA had absolved itself of responsibility for the health of school children.

The Indian Health Service personnel worked with school staff, especially dormitory supervisors, to instruct them in the fundamentals of general health care and first aid. Nonetheless, the school personnel felt great reluctance to play any substantive role in a responsibility which had officially been delegated to another agency. School principals and superintendents pointed with satisfaction to the joint policy statements. Demands for repeated routine examinations met school needs but conflicted with Service Unit priorities. Efforts at establishing joint programs met with little success. At Shiprock we set up a special clinic for the schoolchildren, who could then be processed more rapidly with greater continuity of care. Unfortunately, the easy proximity of the clinic to the school led to overutilization of the clinic for very minor problems which could have been treated at school. A constant and unproductive interchange ensued between the schools, who were reluctant to reduce their demands, and the Service Unit, which could not keep pace.

Dealings with BIA officials were equally frustrating in other areas. A project to install road bumpers at PHS expense to slow traffic on roads jointly controlled by PHS and BIA was ensnarled in masses of red tape. Not only was BIA reluctant to do something concrete, it was unable to let someone else pour cement.

The BIA was to assume an active role in developing the pilot testing of retroreflective collars on animals grazing on the highways. PHS had set up several planning meetings and had arranged consultation with safety engineers and the firm which would supply the materials. The BIA procrastinated in arranging a trial run until Service Unit personnel had to literally take the bull by the horns lest the project die from neglect.

The most complicated and crucial relationship between the health agency and the BIA is in the area of welfare. Actually the interaction is a three-way interchange with the state departments of welfare also playing a pivotal role. Welfare programs for the Navajo are basically those of the states in which they reside, supplemented in part by a BIA program of general assistance. Welfare support in New Mexico and Arizona is generally limited to categorical assistance (old age assistance, aid to the blind, aid to the permanently and totally disabled, and aid to families with dependent children). Thus most applications for assistance originate in the offices of the BIA, to whom the Indian is accustomed to appeal for help. The BIA has customarily been tight-fisted with general assistance beyond acute emergency situations.

Any claim which may involve some element of disability is referred to the Indian Health Service clinic for evaluation. The clinic physician finds himself in a moral mousetrap. His failure to certify the client as disabled will inevitably deny him the welfare assistance he desperately needs. Some physicians who are socially aware are strained to the limits of their professional integrity. In an atmosphere of hectic clinical activity, this sort of philosophic contortion is even less welcome. Nor is the problem limited to original applicants for welfare. Once certified, each disabled recipient (regardless of his disability—the amputee along with the temporarily injured) must return monthly with another batch of forms and be recertified. And what is a disability? The Navajo with arthritis is physically able to work as a bank president, but there are no opportunities for such employment and he has no training for the task.

Experience with the welfare system quickly teaches the doctor that his report may determine the patient's financial future. He also learns that the white bureaucracy, especially the state agencies, are less than sympathetic to the Navajo who seeks help but does not exactly fit the categories established. The physician feels pressured because the patient comes to him, form in hand, with expectations that PHS will get him the help he needs. At the same time, the welfare bureaucrats demand extraneous information, time-consuming to collect, with the implied threat of indefinite procrastination on the case.

Many of the physicians at Shiprock had experiences with more liberal programs of Public Assistance before coming to the Navajo reservation. The Arizona program is a contrast. Recently a HEW hearing examiner presided in San Francisco over a procedure which accused the Arizona Welfare Board of violating federal welfare regulations. Among those testifying was Mrs. Robert Blackgoat, a widow, age 54, with five children and grandchildren to support. Mrs. Blackgoat lived six miles from the nearest water supply and nine miles from the wood supply. Her only income was derived from the annual sale of six to eight sheep from her small flock. Mrs. Blackgoat received $155 a month in the summer (when the children were home), $63 a month during the winter, and no check at all during several autumn months while the Welfare Department calculated the deductions based on her sheep income. Because she purchased a truck in which to haul water and wood to her home, the Welfare Department threatened to cut off her assistance entirely. It is not surprising that welfare experts at the hearing testified that Arizona's welfare requirements "do not comply with humanity or law."

The PHS personnel feel that BIA does not understand the demands on their time when it insists on cumbersome procedures such as continuous disability recertification. However, one must not assume that PHS personnel understand the pressures on the BIA. As an example of how all agencies interact, the legal aid group on the reservation, by organizing welfare rights groups, greatly increased the number of legitimate applicants for general assistance in the last year. The underfunded BIA Social Services program must cope with this inundation and also with the PHS two-year physicians who are willing to bend over backwards to declare applicants eligible. It is easy for each agency to label the other as "the bad guy," especially when no ongoing mechanisms exist for communicating with each other. Parenthetically, we noticed a social distance between BIA and PHS employees, even though they are housed in the same compound.

The local welfare agencies also share responsibility with the BIA Social Service staff in child protection. Frequently the county agencies are under-staffed, underfunded, and under pressure to respond to demands. Torn by conflicting forces, they seek to dump as much as possible on the laps of others. Physicians have been trained to do everything possible for their patients and have a low tolerance of agencies which cannot respond with similar vigor.

On several occasions the pediatricians at Shiprock were convinced that a child's repeated admissions to the hospital were the result of parental neglect. Because it seemed pointless, and perhaps lethal, to return the child to such a dangerous home environment, they requested the welfare agency to take custody of the patient and arrange for foster placement. In view of the difficulty in finding foster homes, the staff time required, and the cost of such maintenance, the agency balked and the children became virtual wards of the hospitals. Friction between the inpatient physicians and the besieged welfare department often produced heated confrontations.

A newer agency on the reservation, funded through grants to the tribe, is the Office of Navajo Economic Opportunity (or ONEO). Like its OEO counterparts elsewhere in the country, ONEO provides a variety of important services. ONEO supports an alcohol treatment program using community workers, many of whom are exalcoholics. The agency stimulated self-help housing projects for which PHS provided sanitary engineering assistance. In keeping with OEO goals, the ONEO focused much of its effort on children. Neighborhood Youth Corps teenagers gained experiences in the multiple health professions, while augmenting the PHS manpower pool. Preschool children were enrolled in the Headstart programs.

In its enthusiasm to see the much needed Headstart schools established, the PHS committed itself to provide medical care for these youngsters. Although a major component of such programs nationally include the purchase of medical and dental care, Headstart on the Navajo reservation did not. When demands for services again exceeded our ability to supply them, we met with local ONEO officials to discuss other possibilities. They were most receptive to the use of private purveyors where available if the Area office would acknowledge the need for such a change. Unfortunately, the Navajo

Area was unwilling to concede their inability to supply the high level care which is a mainstay of the Headstart program. In the end, the children were the losers.

The ONEO also established food programs to supply prepackaged formula to premature infants during their first year of life and to distribute supplemental foods to high-risk persons. The premature infant program can probably be credited with saving lives and certainly with reducing morbidity. As the program gained experience, it spread to take in other high-risk children by providing various special formulas that reduced the morbidity of diarrheal disease.

The supplemental food distribution program is a vivid example of how a bureaucratic structure can impede a needed service. For purposes of this program, "high risk" was defined as children under five and pregnant or lactating women. Although a minimum of clinical acumen is required to establish compliance with such criteria, a physician or public health nurse was required to certify each potential participant monthly. Nobody could explain the need for the extensive forms in multiple copies or the elaborate procedures for obtaining the food. As the consumers began to get discouraged with the new program, the PHS and ONEO met repeatedly to find ways to make so vital a program work. Eventually the impediments were removed and confidence in the program increased.

The ONEO originally sponsored a legal services program for the Navajo. *Dinebeiina Nahilna Be Agaditehe* roughly means "lawyers who work for the economic betterment of the people" and is better known as DNA. In addition to offering legal advice to individuals, DNA also pursued major social issues. The lawyers organized welfare rights groups and publicized alleged practices of traders who cheated their dependent customers. Not surprisingly, these activities soon brought them into conflict with the tribal government. Like the VISTA workers before them, their threat to the establishment produced waves of enmity. Although the tribe was unable to banish the organization from the reservation, it did threaten the funding. DNA support was transferred for a time to the national OEO organization, but recently the money has been returned to regular ONEO channels.

This controversial legal aid group had an effect on all agencies in Shiprock, even PHS. DNA was a harbinger of social change and therefore potentially disruptive. The general attitude of PHS's Area office was one of caution; Area staff deemed it prudent not to establish too much cooperation with the new legal service's program while it was out of favor with elected tribal officials.

One of the most dramatic efforts of DNA lawyers was the battle of the Gallup jail. Gallup is a town of about 10,000 located just off the reservation border. Formerly an important railroad junction, Gallup exists primarily on its trade with the Navajo now that the railroad has dwindled as an economic force. Much of the trade is in alcohol. The town is crammed with bars, and alcoholics often litter the streets after weekend sprees. In the spring of 1970, DNA filed suit against the City of Gallup on behalf of one of the prisoners in the overcrowded jail. The lawyers condemned the unsanitary and unsafe conditions under which alcoholics were crowded into an inadequate jail (sometimes a hundred over capacity) and denied proper care. The suit, complete with movies and site visits, created a national stir. Gallup was ordered to keep its prison population down to the capacity of the prison.

The PHS was involved—in fact, caught in the middle. Although the major medical center for the Navajo Area is located in Gallup, little attention had been paid to the problem of the weekend alcoholics, beyond keeping them out of the hospital lobby. Suddenly the demand was to treat the alcoholic as a patient rather than a criminal. Under fire from the DNA, city officials tried to dump the problem on the hospital's doorstep.

Eventually a compromise was reached. As pressures on the city relaxed, the demands on PHS also eased up. A new jail was scheduled for construction and conditions in the existing facility were improved. The Gallup Indian Hospital speeded its plans for an outpatient alcoholic treatment program. Community agencies including PHS worked together to institute some make-shift arrangements so that drunks could have a place to "sleep it off" other than the jail, the hospital, or the streets.

The attitudes of the border towns are entrenched. As one employee of a Gallup newspaper described the situation, "There is no alcoholism problem [in Gallup], just too many drunk Indians." Indifference to the plight of the Indian often merged with resentment towards a race which doesn't pay taxes but receives welfare. (Such logic ignores the average family income of only $1,200 a year.)

Another border town which loudly deplored the financial burden of the alcoholic Navajo was equally pleased to take Navajo money. The town officials constantly pointed to the fact that Navajos cost the town money in law enforcement. When confronted with the fact that ten million dollars was spent in town annually by reservation dwellers, the city fathers admitted that the association brought more economic benefit than burden. Yet the attitude of resentment persisted despite the city's dependency on the Navajos.

Although Shiprock is a population center of approximately five thousand, it is not incorporated as a municipality. There is no provision for town government, collection of taxes, or institution of services. The businesses in Shiprock are located there through lease agreements with the Navajo tribe as approved by the BIA. Shiprock residents are forced to go to the off-reservation cities for much of their shopping and entertainment. Gradually a mutually dependent relationship has evolved which is characterized by hostility on both sides.

An issue which particularly produced difficulties between Shiprock and the neighboring city was the dispute over the use of contract medical care (CMC) funds. Historically, the physicians of these towns had provided the bulk of whatever medical care the Navajos received. As the PHS developed and improved medical facilities on the reservation, more of the care could be provided at PHS installations and contract expenditures were reduced. Further budgetary restrictions in the face of rising medical costs forced the review of contract medical care priorities, already described. One of the areas of restriction was nonemergency outpatient visits. Physicians could no longer be assured of PHS reimbursement for the care of colds and sore throats at an off-reservation hospital. The local hospital's emergency room was in a bind. It could not turn away anyone lest he be seriously ill, but it would not be paid except for true emergencies. The decision was a policy of active discouragement.

Another point of controversy arose over the responsibility for the medical care of prisoners in local police custody. Federal regulations prohibited the use of CMC funds for the treatment of Indians in the custody of non-Indian police. The local constabulary was unwilling to assume responsibility. Police medical funds were extended to those who injured themselves in jail, but did not cover treatment of a chronic or pre-existing condition, such as epilepsy. In an effort to force the local governments to share some responsibility for the Indians who help support the towns, the Service Unit held fast to the regulation. The police had to assume costs or transport the prisoner to Shiprock. At first delighted by the opportunity to avoid fiscal responsibility for some segment of medical care, the Area office supported this position; but as political pressure grew, the Area reversed itself and absolved the local police of the obligation.

In its capacity as third-party sponsor for medical care, the Indian Health Service was responsible for assuring the quality of care purchased. Rarely was this charge faced in anything more than a superficial manner. In general, the medical profession is a tight guild which is reluctant to police itself and very resentful of others who try to do it for them.

On two occasions the Service Unit staff attempted to intervene on behalf of a patient who had received very unsatisfactory care. One elderly physician in the neighboring town was notorious for his willingness to provide injectable antibiotics on request (and after payment). Frequently he did not see the patient but left his nurse to render the diagnosis and treatment herself. A young Navajo child was admitted to the PHS hospital late one evening with symptoms of acute meningitis. The family gave a history of having visited the physician in question the previous day with the child, who then had similar symptoms. The nurse had treated the child with a little-used antibiotic and sent him home. A call to the doctor's office corroborated the family's history.

This partial treatment had not only delayed adequate therapy to a life-threatening condition, but also made identification of the etiologic organism impossible. For these reasons we brought the case to the attention of the county medical society. The physician had been a potent force in the society for many years. Despite our inquiries about the case, the matter was dropped. The doctor continued to dispense antibiotics with his former indiscretion.

Our second effort to encourage the profession to police itself concerned a young child who was transferred from the local hospital to the PHS hospital when the emergency nature of the infant's condition had apparently subsided. Reviewing the hospital record, we found a number of serious inadequacies. Although the child had been admitted for an infection of unknown origin, no studies had been done to seek the etiology. Even an x-ray of the chest had been delayed for several days. Instead of intravenous feeding, the physician had used clysis—a method of subcutaneous fluid therapy generally abandoned a generation ago. No electrolyte studies had been done to monitor the effects of this feeding. Potent and dangerous antibiotics had been used without apparent justification. When the patient arrived at our facility, she was severely dehydrated and in metabolic imbalance.

After treating the child for her illness and the iatrogenic disorders, we debated our course of action. Frustrated by our previous attempt to criticize a local practitioner, we elected to consult with the pediatric specialist at the off-reservation hospital. He confirmed our impression of mismanagement and referred to other examples he had witnessed. On his recommendation we requested a hearing before the professional board of the hospital. At the hearing we explained our concern about the specific case and the general problem of assuring quality care for our beneficiaries. The board agreed to discuss the case but was disinterested in any continuing action on the problem of auditing care.

Several weeks later we received a one-sentence letter from the board stating that it had met. No mention of any decision or action was made. At the same time the board demanded from the Area director that he curb those Service Unit personnel who had the effrontery to tell the town how to practice medicine. The director assured the board that our intentions were good and apologized. We were warned not to antagonize private practitioners further.

We had succeeded in proving our inability to exact any quality standards in the care we were financing. If we could not stop overt abuses, certainly we were powerless to influence the subtle prejudices which the neighboring townsmen held towards Navajos. These biases necessarily crept into medical care. On one occasion a Navajo was involved in an accident near the city and hospitalized in the intensive care unit for some weeks until he could be moved. He was transferred to the Shiprock hospital with a large bill and his medical record. The latter noted that the patient did not speak English. The patient was a college graduate who happened to be unconscious at the time of of his first admission!

The Service Unit walks a tight-rope in dealing with the various agencies and factions both in Shiprock and in the off-reservation towns. Conceivably, the entire time of an administrator could be spent in relating to the existing structure. Although time-consuming, the relationships have taken on a ritualized quality, as though everyone finds repetition of the same problems and statements of policy or limitation rather reassuring.

Any changes, contemplated or real, within the medical system bring a reaction from the various other systems. Usually, elaborate preparation of outside interests is useful before making a change within one's own jurisdiction. And the utmost diplomacy is required in trying to adjust an ongoing arrangement between one's agency and another group. Sometimes, however, especially in relation to the institutions which are off the reservation, the most extensive efforts at discussion and cooperation cannot cut through layers of prejudice.

In working with community agencies and factions, we have observed a variation of Robert Frost's adage; seemingly, in interagency relations, good fence-sitting makes good neighbors. The genuine need for good working relations with all elements in the community must be balanced with the need to develop a creative, dynamic program which is truly responsive to community health needs.

Chapter XI
M.D. or Not M.D.

For generations the medical profession has been dominated by the physician. The extent of the domination is evidenced by the almost synonymous connotation of "physicians" and "medical profession." With the appearance of new health professionals and the resurgence of some old ones, new terms like "paramedicals" had to be created. The "paramedical," as the word suggests, works alongside the doctor, rendering peripheral services to support the physician in his role of supplying the primary medical care.

More and more, we are being forced to question what is "para" and what is "medical." New health professionals are gaining more and more access to the patient and physicians are more and more assuming roles which do not call for direct medical care. The team concept has gained increasing popularity in the drive for comprehensive, coordinated and continuous patient care. Almost universally, the physician is perceived as the captain of the team.

The Service Unit in the Indian Health Service is a very large team; the qualifications and background of its captain will have much to do with the direction the unit takes. The question of whether the chief administrator, the Service Unit director, need be or even should be a physician is relevant to many aspects of administration today.

The hospital administrator, *per se*, is not generally a physician. The majority of hospitals across the country are directed by professional administrators whose task is to run the hospital system as efficiently and effectively as possible. But the physicians remain outside that hospital system. They attend patients in their hospital workshop but are rarely controlled by its administration in any meaningful sense.

The Indian Health Service's hospital systems differ. The physicians are salaried staff members who are contained within the hospital system. This model is not the common one across the nation, although the same structure prevails in prepaid practices and in other government programs such as the Veteran's Administration. The question becomes one of who should adminis-

121

ter the hospital when that administrator will also be the doctors' boss.

Although most Service Unit directors in the Indian Health Service are physicians, the agency, since 1966, has appointed other kinds of professionals to the position. In the Navajo Area, 1969, two Service Unit directors were not doctors—one was a pharmacist by training and the other a hospital administrator. Both of these men operated rather small Service Units and both seemed to be accepted by their staff (1).

In appointing nonphysicians as Service Unit directors, the Indian Health Service was providing career opportunities for some of its permanent employees while attempting to reduce the high turnover in leadership which occurred when two-year men were given the positions. At the same time, they could reduce the manpower drain from the often-dry physician pool.

One former nonphysician Service Unit director recalls countless examples of good physicians who became very poor Service Unit directors and unhappy men.

Three interrelated aspects of the administrator's role may be separated out, at least for the purposes of discussion. We may consider whether the physician or some other person is best equipped to manage the interdisciplinary group which makes up the Service Unit and to balance the curative and preventive programs within the system. Secondly, we may look at the Service Unit director's role as spokesman for the agency in the community and think what background might produce the most effective dealings with consumers and community leaders. Finally, we might ask what administrator is best able to relate to the physicians among the staff.

Who is best fit to be captain of a team which will contain members who, by training and temperament, consider themselves team captains? At first glance, it seems that the physician-administrator is in an advantageous position to develop close working relationships with the ruling class of medical care, the doctors. He speaks their language, he shares their cultural heritage, he has had at least an introduction to clinical medicine.

Yet the physicians do not necessarily accept the idea of one of their own as the team captain. A team composed only of quarterbacks may have great difficulty in getting organized to allow one person to call the plays. Physicians are accustomed to a command role and often have a hard time accepting orders or suggestions from either peers or consumers. The physician who is well skilled in more traditional clinical areas may be mistrusted when he enters the alien world of administration. More dangerous, he may mistrust himself and thus fail to take a decisive stand when dealing with the other doctors.

The physician-administrator who lacks clinical skill and training runs the risk of being dismissed by his peers as an incompetent colleague who has opted for a face-saving way out. Indeed, for too long administration as well as public health has been the perennial refuge of the retired, disabled, or incompetent physician. The development of a cadre of skilled young M.D.'s with advanced training in administration and/or public health is a relatively new phenomenon, poorly understood by the medical profession. The physician who decides to devote his career to administration or planning of medical services must guard against being open to accusations of clinical incompetence. Yet, however he works to keep up, it is obvious that his clinical skills will necessarily take second place to other kinds of specialized knowledge more central to his task. The average physician doubts the existence of such a body of knowledge.

The physician who finds himself in this quandary (especially if he has been promoted from the ranks to Service Unit director and has had no particular training in medical care administration) may seek refuge in more accustomed pursuits and identities. He may try to prove his professional stature by entering the arena of practice. Depending on the size of the operation, this may or may not be an affordable luxury. Time spent with individual patients usually means time lost from the primary mission of organization and leadership. While in some instances clinical work may be a deliberate device to gain the respect of the physicians, such activity threatens the administrator's position as administrator. He may become overly identified with the physician group in the delicate balance of power; more importantly, the daily pressure to see patients and meet their immediate needs may cause him to lose his perspective on the overall operations of his unit. While a limited amount of patient contact may be helpful to keep one's foot in reality, a constant exposure may direct inappropriate attention to short-term needs, a tendency which is already accentuated by medical education.

In some settings, particularly in the Indian Health Service, the inadequate staffing patterns may precipitate this dilemma. Insufficient medical staff under heavy pressure to meet the immediate demands for service may balk at the idea of one of their number abstracting himself from clinical duties to pursue planning. In this same context, we found that the physicians at Shiprock were highly intolerant of the idea that one of the doctors should direct the field health program rather than see patients. The clinicians solved this problem by perceiving the role of field medical officer in terms of a physician who treated specified groups of patients (school children, patients in outlying clinics) rather than the director of a preventive program. This attitude of the doctors became a self-fulfilling prophecy. Especially since he lacked any training or experience in administration, the field medical officer was unable to assert himself in directing the program but tried to conform to patterns expected by the other physicians.

Our own experience highlights the problems of exercising leadership over other physicians. The author's predecessor was in the unlucky position of being neither a clinical nor a public health specialist. (He had advanced through the "promotion by attrition" phenomenon.) Since he could not seek refuge in practice of a clinical specialty, he busied himself in administrative details of budgeting and disbursement of funds, becoming a bureaucrat's bureaucrat with little rapport with the other doctors. When he left, a one-month hiatus ensued during which the Service Unit was without a director.

Upon arrival, the new Service Unit director was greeted by the news that the doctors had accomplished more in the past month than had been accomplished all year. He was told that a new spirit of cooperation and joint planning existed and was invited not to rock the boat. In an offhand manner, his name had been added to the list of doctors performing night duty.

In reality the doctors had accomplished little in terms of planning for the entire range of services and disciplines under the Service Unit umbrella. They had freed themselves of a leader they did not respect and felt that no new leader was necessary. When it became clear that the new Service Unit director did not intend to take a night call rotation, the resentment was keen. This issue did not really die though it eventually became less intense as it became apparent that the Service Unit director did put in as many hours as anybody else and was unable to commit himself to a regular evening on call because of other demands on his time. It seemed to us that the complaints, half jocular, half serious, about the Service Unit director's avoidance of night duty petered out as the physicians began to recognize that he did indeed have his own sphere of expertise in the field of medical planning.

Physicians do tend to respect competence and have a high intolerance for what they perceive as incompetence. Eventually they will accept leadership from a physician who has shown an expertise in administration. In all probability they will relate better to such an able physician-administrator than to a nonphysician. But physicians with training and inclination for administration are relatively few. A competent administrator is preferable to a physician who is floundering. The latter is likely to be controlled by the physicians in subtle ways.

Working and living in relative isolation also influences the physician-administrator. His relationships with the other doctors are not purely professional but social as well. The other physicians are most likely to share his background and interests. Problems which develop at the hospital cannot be left behind very readily, but tend to reappear at the dinner and bridge tables. The administrator may find himself choosing a relatively restricted social life in order to avoid conflicts in social-professional relationships.

This problem is most severe when the administrator is not secure in his own expertise. If the administrator is confident of his ability, he should be no more suggestible than the surgeon or pediatrician would be at the hands of a colleague from another specialty. We have met physician-Service Unit directors who have made it a policy not to mingle socially with the other physicians, especially in small groups. Such a policy seems to cut the administrator off from communication channels and negate one of the natural advantages of having an M.D. in charge.

We have labored the point of competence. We must now consider what constitutes competence in a Service Unit director and under what conditions the physician fits the requirements.

The physician-administrator starts out with several advantages over someone without medical training. Ideally, the physician has acquired a broad understanding of medical problems as well as a practical appreciation of the difficulties associated with the delivery of good medical care. As a physician, he is perhaps more likely to focus on the patient than on the system or the providers. This patient orientation can be an asset. Too often an administrator may get trapped into an emphasis on the efficiency of an operation until he eventually loses sight of the reason for the system in the first place—the patient population and its needs.

On the other hand, the physician's training in patient care may offer a serious handicap. While he may have a greater appreciation of the variety of illnesses that plague his constituents, his one-to-one experience with the treatment of disease may hinder him from comprehending the broader scope of health problems which he faces. Curative medicine may dominate the pattern of services to the detriment of other approaches such as preventive and environmental services.

On numerous occasions we came to appreciate the ease with which preventive services could be defined in terms of curative care. Given the opportunity, the physicians encouraged the public health nurses to expend their efforts in facilitating treatment programs by rendering home care, transporting patients or delivering messages and medicines. In such cases, the physicians perceived the preventive apparatus as a defender of the hospital and clinics; that is, they supported those activities which might tend to reduce the patient's need to come to the hospital. But health goals can and should be formulated in broader terms to embrace the overall impact of the program on the health of a community. The administrator, whatever his discipline, must be able to keep these larger goals in mind.

The physician is by training (and perhaps by self-selection) a rather pragmatic individual. He is accustomed to seeing an immediate result from his efforts. The patient may recover or worsen, but something happens. Gratification, for the clinician, depends upon his own awareness of services well performed and upon the patient's appreciation. Both sources of satisfaction depend upon relatively rapid and direct feedback. On the other hand, the administrator is more often involved in programs which evolve over long periods during which a multiplicity of forces shape and alter the original design. Many of his policies are efforts to avoid consequences rather than to create them, as for example in preventive programs to reduce disease. The physician who has been accustomed to taking decisive action with dramatic results may transfer his clinical outlook to his administrative post.

Nothing in a physician's training or experience prepares him for a self-effacing role. On the contrary, we have noted that physicians tend to develop authoritarian personalities, leading (sometimes ignoring) their teams with a confident sense of omniscience (2). As an administrator, the physician is called upon to encourage others of many diverse disciplines in reaching their fullest potential. Such a transition is not simple for an individual to make. Furthermore, in clinical practice the physician's sense of accomplishment is fed by general recognition of his deeds. The best administrators are those who can stimulate the deeds of others and allow others to take the bows.

The individual in charge of a large health program will continuously be faced with decisions on the allocation of material and human resources. He will often be called upon to assign priorities. Little in medical school equips a physician to make decisions on the basis of reasoned probabilities. After the individual diagnosis is made, the doctor is conditioned to strive heroically for each patient. The administrator must first consider his manpower, with the realization that a resource expended in one direction is a resource unavailable for some other activity. He may have to make difficult decisions to abandon one health goal in pursuit of another more rewarding one. A physician-administrator who is attuned to the clinical model may endlessly avoid such priority-setting. Instead he may refuse to accept limitations for any goal, least of all the concrete clinical services. Without conscious efforts to set priorities, indirect preventive services are likely to suffer.

"BELIEVE ME, MISTER, THERE'S NO NEGLECT LIKE BENIGN NEGLECT."

The combined experience of medical school, internship, and clinical residency, then, does not produce an ideal constellation of characteristics and habits for a medical administrator. Yet the physician has too great a potential as a planner to be readily abandoned. The patient-orientation of the physician is still a very important point in his favor. The administrator who does not have a thorough background in medicine may pursue efficiency as a sterile end-goal. His instincts to evaluate effectiveness may be faulty.

From time to time various proponents of physician-administrator programs have suggested specially tailored training programs which would allow candidates to deviate from traditional clinical training for more intense preparation in administrative techniques. These proposals do have appeal. Early differentiation of career pathways promises to shorten the training period for physician-administrators while at the same time providing them with the background to function effectively.

On the other hand this deviation from the clinical pathway may risk rejection by both camps. In the eyes of clinicians, the products will be second-rate doctors, and to professional administrators they will be only slightly polished physicians. We believe that the physician-administrator definitely requires specific training but would be wary of an early separation of prospective clinicians from prospective administrators during the medical school years. Such a sorting system would be bound to place administrators on a lower rung of the hierarchy.

Moreover, without attempting to turn all physicians into experts in medical care delivery, we would like all medical students to receive some introduction into the issues of medical care so that they might understand and cooperate with the efforts of the skilled administrator. This object would not be served by early separation of potential administrators from the flock of students.

What knowledge is essential to the health administrator? Bearing in mind that no individual could hope to retain a fraction of available medical lore, perhaps an important piece of knowledge is simply knowing how to tap available and pertinent information. A background in epidemiology is helpful since epidemiology is the application of scientific methods to the study of disease. Some understanding of economics is also useful. But perhaps the most important knowledge, for a creative and dynamic administrator, is an understanding of health services research. An administrator should be able to make use of past health services research, evaluate ongoing efforts, and be able to stimulate and direct research into delivery methods within his own institution.

Other theoretical equipment for the administrator might include a knowledge of group process and some understanding on which to predict human behavior. On the practical side, knowledge of sources of medical funding and the art of grantsmanship should be part of the administrator's equipment.

In the last analysis, attitudes are probably more important than knowledge. The administrator needs to be poised between the preventive and the curative services. He needs to be able to think of statistics and probabilities without losing grasp of the fact that patients are people with emotional as well as physical needs. He needs to struggle towards efficiency without forgetting that a medical system must be efficient in terms of realizing its goals for betterment of the community's health. And he must have a broad concept of health which reaches far beyond hospital walls and present health services.

If the administrator manages to be all of this, it hardly matters whether he is a physician by original training. A conventionally trained physician may have to struggle against all his instincts to serve as an administrator, and a good clinician is wasted when he is thrust into the role. A specially trained physician may be the ideal Service Unit director but other professionals may also serve effectively in medical planning and administration.

REFERENCES

1. Knight, J. I. The non-physician Service Unit director concept. Paper presented at the PHS Clinical Society Meeting. Washington, D.C., April, 1970.
2. Kane, R. & Kane, R. Physicians' attitudes of omnipotence in a university hospital. *Journal of Medical Education.* 1969, *44:* 684-690.

Chapter XII

Implications for a National Health Corps

In the United States today—the wealthiest nation in the history of man—millions of our citizens are sick. And they are sick because they are poor. The sickness is the shame of America. Of all the faces of poverty, the sickness of the poor is the ugliest. Of all the effects of poverty, it is the sickness of the poor that we could attack most easily, had we the will (1).

—Senator Edward Kennedy

Senator Edward Kennedy suggested a means to attack the sickness of the poor in his cosponsorship of the Senate Bill S-4106, "Introduction of the National Health Service Corps Act of 1970." This is not the first bill of its kind, nor is it likely to be the last.* Each year, as medical costs rise, the discrepancy between the care available to the several classes of our "classless society" is more apparent. Methods of approach, particularly Medicaid, have not appreciably narrowed the gap. In areas where the Medicaid program has been heavily instituted, the change generated more cost than care. Essentially the same treatment was provided at grossly inflated fees. Although new money was pumped into the medical system, the system remained virtually unchanged.

Another cosponsor of Bill S-4106, Senator Magnuson, envisages the Corps as an instructive experience:

What the Corps will do is to provide us with greater practical experience in meeting the health care needs of the poor. It is this experience that we will have to draw on in the years ahead,

---

*This bill has now been passed into law as the "Emergency Health Personnel Act" of 1970.

whether the ultimate answer lies in the government or private sector, or somewhere in between (2).

We already have some "practical experience" in this type of situation. It would appear most impractical not to examine the Indian Health Service with reference to immediate and ultimate implications for a National Health Corps. Under the administrative umbrella of the Indian Health Service, medical care is provided for widely dispersed groups of patients who vary greatly in culture, tradition, and present needs both from each other and from middle-class American norms. The various beneficiary groups do have one thing in common besides original land titles to the continent—the individuals and the societies are poor to an extent unequalled anywhere in the United States. Presumably a National Health Corps would also serve groups with distinctive cultural features and widely divergent life-styles, from rural to inner-city urban. The target groups would differ from each other and from the American mainstream, but they would all share the poor health opportunities which accompany poverty.

The history of the Indian Health Service under PHS is relatively brief, yet many of the lessons learned should be transferable.

First we must distinguish between programs of medical care like the proposed National Health Service Corps and more comprehensive programs such as the Indian Health Service. The latter includes activities in environmental health, nutrition, health education, and public health nursing, as well as the direct medical services. This distinction is important in defining the scope of the proposals under discussion and in providing some appropriate expectations.

We are much wiser about how to make people ill than how to keep them well.* We know that too much or too little food produces various states of malnutrition, but we do not know how to influence a population to eat properly. We have identified a variety of deleterious influences on chronic disease—from anxiety to smoking—but are quite naive about how to use this information. In more rational moments, we acknowledge that the great impact on disease has been the result of socioeconomic forces. A proposal for a National Health Service Corps to treat the poor is an indirect acknowledgment of the bond between health and economics. It is more feasible and more

---

*We deliberately avoid use of the word "healthy" because of the interminable discussions one encounters over the WHO definition of "health"—"a state of complete physical, mental, and social well-being and not merely the absence of disease or infirmity."

acceptable to devise programs to treat the diseases of the poor than the societal diseases which make them poor to begin with.

Perhaps our distinction between curative and comprehensive programs is somewhat overdrawn. An OEO program in Mississippi began with a focus on basic medical care, but soon discovered that food was its most potent drug (3). The treatment approach quickly centered around ways to get the target group better fed. But this flexibility is not always easily achieved, depending as it does on the climate within the health agency itself and within the surrounding community.

A curative program for the poor is a worthwhile goal in itself; we do not mean to minimize the need to treat disease. Yet it is entirely possible that a Health Corps working in poverty areas would soon identify issues that would threaten the entire health establishment in the United States and even the larger social, political, and economic fabric of which health care is a part. It is not hard to imagine idealistic, young health professionals developing public pressure against local welfare officials for withholding food stamps, or organizing miners to strike for better health and disability benefits. Aspects of the welfare system based on arbitrary definitions of total and permanent disability may readily become sources of conflict. The harsh reactions of school officials to adolescents' use of drugs may be criticized and opposed. Wherever health impinges on sociopolitical issues, we might anticipate that at least some of the young professionals will antagonize established officialdom.

If Congress enters the field of health planning, it should spell out its expectations for the program. Is a National Health Corps, for example, to publicize controversial issues? Is it to develop medical techniques which are a departure from conventional modes? If such decisions are treated honestly and openly both with prospective employees and prospective consumers, the program stands a better chance of success.

As we have observed in connection with the Indian Health Service, such basic issues of purpose and limitations are obscured in rhetoric and red tape. The stated goals of the Indian Health Service do call for "Indian involvement and participation." The phrase sounds impressive but is too vague to be useful. Indian societies have their own power structures, sometimes out of tune with the poorest members of the group. If the involvement is only to be with Indian officials, it is analogous to asking President Nixon to serve as consumer representative for a health program in a Washington ghetto.

Although the Indian Health Service does not spell out which Indians are to be involved, the ground rules for the Navajo Area were seemingly clear. After a few experiences, one surmises that the object is to render as competent care as possible without antagonizing any power within or around the Navajo communities. Unfortunately, the pool of personnel drawn from applicants to the two-year military deferment plan tended to be men who could not live with these limited goals. Either they fought the system or lapsed into bored apathy.

In all likelihood the new National Health Corps would recruit doctors from the same pool as the Indian Health Service, perhaps with a similar military service aspect. These young men would be working in situations of greater sensitivity and less isolation from public attention than those working on Indian reservations. It would be imperative for them to know the ground rules from the beginning. If the program is meant to avoid political entanglements, the personnel should be informed. If the aim is to be innovative professionally and fearless politically, the employees should be assured backup support. But if the rhetoric of the program ends up deceiving its own staff, the disillusionment that follows will be fast, furious, and likely fatal to the morale of the agency.

Moving from the clarification of goals to the actual implementation of a program which is both curative and preventive, the Indian Health Service points up additional problems. We noted a great deal of resentment on the part of those working within curative programs towards those whose efforts had more long-range potential. In the abstract, the providers of care would generally acknowledge that preventive and public health measures had the greatest chance of making an impact on the health of the community. Under the stress of daily work, they only saw the diversion of resources from the clinical struggle in progress.

Health teams are very much in vogue, and the idea is sound. But despite the talk of health teams, teamwork will not arise spontaneously. The various members must share a philosophical approval of the idea of the team, but they must be "coached" before they learn how to work individually with their team-mates. Cooperation cannot occur without respect, and respect depends on an understanding of what each person can contribute to the overall effort. The respect is most important when the pressure is on, but must be worked at during the lulls. To extend the team sport analogy, the team must practice so that, under pressure, team functioning will become a reflex.

Too often, the assumption is that a gathering of different professionals automatically constitutes a team. Also too often, as pressures within a program grow and money and time tighten, the first activities to be abandoned are education and communication within the staff. Education is necessary to inform all members of the team about the contributions, actual or potential, of the others. Communication is imperative to reinforce that awareness and retain the team approach.

Any program which delivers services faces problems of recruiting and retaining personnel. Perhaps the retention of staff is the most important for both the consumers and the providers. For the consumers, a constant parade of new faces destroys the continuity of care and underlines the depersonalization of their experiences in other aspects of life. Continuously we heard Navajos deploring the lack of "a doctor" with whom they could form a lasting relationship. They interpreted the short tenure as lack of genuine concern and quickly assumed that the assignments were part of a young physician's training period. Not surprisingly, even nonsurgical patients sought out the one Navajo surgeon whose long training was generally known and whose dedication to the region was indisputable.

The agency itself finds constant turnover disruptive. The new men must be orientated, which is always time-consuming. One of the cliches of administration suggests that a long time elapses before a new man can be genuinely productive. This verdict is an oversimplification—often a new employee is at his most productive when his enthusiasm is highest. It does take time, however, before a new man fits smoothly into the team machinery and if too many team members are new, much continuity is lost. Also, with constant turnover the employees lose the individual satisfactions derived from longterm patient relationships or the completion of a project.

Many institutions, created in a spirit of excitement, attract staff who are enthusiastic for the new project. Yet the zeal wanes in the first exposure to the monumental obstacles to be overcome. OEO funded neighborhood health centers have already experienced this phenomenon, as staff members depart to try new unchallenged sites.

There is little doubt that today's students express a social consciousness well byond that of earlier cohorts. In many there exists a readily perceived desire, if not a compulsion, to be of positive service to less advantaged groups. The bulk of this motivation has been created in the abstract and has yet to be tested in actual service. Senator Kennedy expresses optimism over the coming confrontation:

> Once young Corps physicians are exposed to the problems of health care in poverty areas, I believe that a significant number of them will be encouraged to remain and dedicate their careers to this service, to the lasting benefit of the health of America (4).

Many social scientists are less optimistic. They warn of the job frustrations to be encountered and the probable lack of job satisfaction unless new frameworks are devised. Indian Health Service experience would tend to confirm the pessimistic view. The majority of two-year men do not remain, in either private or government capacities, to continue the fight to improve the Indian's health. It seems unlikely that mere exposure to a problem will produce a marked change in career plans. Unfortunately, little data is available on attitudinal changes as a result of such experiences, nor are there experiments which test the effect of different types of administrative support on the personnel. Observations of other professional groups which deal daily with the frustrations of multiple problem families offer little solace. "Police brutality" and the indifferent bureaucracy of many public social service agencies are grim reminders of possible results of simple exposure to persistent problems.

The same factors that make the inhabitants anxious to escape poverty areas will influence the providers. Filth and squalor cannot be fully counteracted by shiny health facilities. The frustrations of dealing with multiple physical and social problems simultaneously may prove too much for the providers. In the rural settings the isolation may become intolerable with time, whereas in the urban settings, staff may remove themselves socially and psychologically from the target areas. The lack of visible progress, moreover, will discourage all but the most committed.

If upon these difficulties is lowered an administrative structure which is both unrewarding and restrictive, the pressures to leave will be great indeed. Bureaucratic regimentation and stifling of creativity could make the situation unbearable for those who came with an impetus to serve. Administration must find ways to insure that staff members experience some measure of success and must be careful to acknowledge good efforts whenever possible. Plans for relatively isolated projects should include means of providing stimulation other than that generated by the work itself.*

Another element in personnel retention is the fact that permanent staff are likely to move up the organization to positions of administration or greater responsibility in other installations. If promotion and advancement are dependent on moving, continuity and competence become incompatible. In an organization with a high turnover rate like the Indian Health Service, the situation is even more exaggerated. The ability of the service segment to

---

*Experience at the Western Electric factory near Chicago in the 1920's is still relevant today. These observations, known as the Hawthorne effect, suggested that no matter what change occurred, the work output improved. The fact that someone was interested enough to intervene stimulated production.

sustain competent staff is severely threatened. Those who elect to remain at that level face having less competent superiors and possibly loss of rewards such as salary, travel, and prestige.

One alternative is to put the thrust of competency at the service level, and to reward achievements without transfer. In another chapter we discussed the hypothetical elimination of much of the middleman apparatus in the Indian Health Service. A new program could be created without the equivalent of the Indian Health Service's Area offices. Ironically, the concept of "continuity of care" is probably more important in Indian groups and other poverty areas than it is for the middle-class American. One-fifth of the nation makes a major move every year; in lower income groups major moves are less common despite frequent address changes. Yet private practitioners tend to remain in an area, nonetheless, to build up a clientele and a reputation. It is even more important for public services to build up a good reputation, since the clientele tends to be suspicious. The image of any program is not enhanced by frequent personnel changes.

Medical providers are not the only group undergoing changes in social values. The power and desire for power of the medical consumer seems to increase daily. The old reverence for the family doctor has disappeared (along with the kindly family friend who made house calls) to be replaced by a healthy skepticism for the entire medical profession. Perhaps the skepticism is greatest among minority and lower-income groups who have seen the unfriendliest face of modern medicine. Lately, demand for consumer representation on policy-making boards is part of every new proposal. The role of the consumer can no longer be ignored or carelessly inserted in the package as a sign of good will.

We have already touched on the various roles that consumers can play, but some repetition is necessary to appreciate the implications of the question for a national health program.

Consumers can be policy-makers. Indeed, depending on one's definition of "consumer" and "policy," we have long had examples of such activities in the health field. Boards of trustees for hospitals and charitable organizations are usually composed of lay people. In voluntary hospitals, the consumer-trustee is likely to turn up as a patient also. In his board member role, he will probably be quite secure and willing to accept expert advice from health professionals. In many private charitable organizations, the lay board members are not from the beneficiary population. With the advent of OEO programs, the actual consumers of goods and services have been brought more into the planning arena.

Gradually advisory boards have been given or have usurped more and more decision-making power. Often they formulate policy and override executive decisions. Anyone who has been scanning the daily newspapers for the past few years is aware that the consumer boards have run into difficulties. Either the need to find community leaders capable of the responsibility produces a nonrepresentative board or the genuine representatives stagger under the challenge. Training programs may work with the latter group to improve their skills in decision-making; but the more such people are trained the less they are representative.

Consumers can also serve in an advisory and consultative capacity, identifying problems that their constituents have found in getting service and pinpointing unmet needs. Consumer-advisors can use their board positions to publicize their program and its gaps. For best results in this role, we should seek those who have the best communication with the community and can most eloquently articulate the difficulties identified.

A third use of consumers—not often admitted—is to placate the community. Impotent to effect change, the board members become figureheads. Such diversionary tactics may arise through deliberate maneuvering of an unsophisticated population or through default of a group to form a genuine advisory or policy-making board. Even this last type of consumer board can be more than a mere pacifier. For many people health seems to be an issue around which to rally and such boards may be used to train and develop potential community leaders. Thus while many consumer boards are impotent for their overt purpose, they are potentially powerful springboards for the future.

How does this scheme fit into a federal medical program? If a board is to assume a policy-making role in an agency such as the Indian Health Service, special problems emerge. The flow of power in most federal programs is from the top down. Regulations and policies are developed centrally and generally take precedence over local decisions, whether the latter are made by program directors or boards. If real power is to lie with a local board, it cannot be bound by volumes of federal regulations on how to proceed under every conceivable circumstance. But it is hard to imagine a federally-financed, federally-staffed program operating without at least a modicum of regulations and procedures to assure uniformity. It is this uniformity which will inhibit local individualization of programs. One cannot confront unique situations with hard-and-fast rules. We concede the legitimate role of the federal mechanism to exert standards. The challenge for future agencies is to achieve a standard of quality while permitting diversified programs.

Meanwhile methods must be developed to facilitate consumer challenge of existing regulations. Otherwise the administrators find themselves doubly vulnerable; they must respond to the boards, which increasingly will have power to hire and fire, while responding to the regulations of the hierarchy which determines promotions.

We might note that productive consumer involvement is most difficult to achieve at the outset of a program. The introduction of a consumer board as the first step in establishing a service implies a great amount of additional work for the pioneers. Since there has been no traditional role for the consumers or providers, everyone is grappling with role definitions as well as the problems at hand. The insecurity and inexperience of the consumer board may create unnecessary impediments. Nonetheless the direction of political commitment and consumer pressure is clear. The consumer must be involved from the onset. Perhaps the difficulties might be minimized if all parties approached the new program with the honest admission that mistakes are to be expected and that changes are possible.

Effective work with consumers requires a redefinition of the concept of a medical "problem." Too often problems are defined in terms of possible solutions. For example, what community would not declare it needs a new hospital or more doctors? The region might be more efficiently and effectively served by a determination of what actual services are sought and needed. Then a plan might be designed to fill the need. The "hospital" may become a chronic care facility or an emergency clinic and the "doctors" may be home health aides or physician's assistants.

When problems are defined as solutions, opinions become fixed and opportunities for constructive examination of the situation and satisfactory reconciliation of all parties diminish rapidly. But the boards can appropriately help to identify the problem, require the health experts to develop alternative solutions, and then react to and modify the plans offered. Both professional and consumer groups may thus retain their separate identities without threat and each can do the thing it does best.

If consumers can find a role which allows them participation in a meaningful way, other problems may be minimized or eliminated. Opinions will be and always are mixed on the question of whether health care for the poor should be free. In the Indian Health Service we frequently heard the position that the PHS medicine is not valued because it is free. We agree that any setup which takes on the attributes of a "free handout" usually is not highly esteemed. But people involved in a program are more likely to respect and value it. If consumers value the care for its own sake, they need not pay for it to appreciate it and utilize it properly. Token payments, which cost more to collect than the generated revenue, are hard to justify, except as the only possible method to counter overutilization. Surely consumer participation is a more desirable alternative to try first.

In the case of the proposed National Health Corps or other proposals for improving the health care of the poor, one must seriously question whether more physicians will solve the problems. We know that there is some relationship between life-style and health status. Life-style similarly seems to exert a profound effect on an individual's ability to utilize medical care services. Yet it is often assumed that the health problems of the poor will respond to a middle-class solution.

When health professionals have the tables turned and are forced to become patients, they quickly realize how much the system is oriented towards the convenience of the providers. The poor constitute the class that exhibits the greatest difficulty in coping with the environment, both physically and socially. When they evidence the same inabilities in dealing with the medical care system, we counter by various adjustments aimed at preserving the system. Modifications have been tried in various places. Increasing cadres of aides and ancillary workers have been added, but the basic design remains—it is physician-oriented. Whenever the "team" is discussed, few dispute his right to be captain, coach, and quarterback; frequently he is also the major stockholder and almost always is paid as the super-star.

Doctors are expensive to train and to maintain. They require entourages and mechanized support. They tend to cluster together in populous areas. They are trained more for the exotic than the common. They are hard to standardize but are given to compulsive individual routines. Ought we not try to find a more malleable material to work with if we are to remold the medical system? Furthermore, if many of the traditional functions of the physician were assumed by less sophisticated paraprofessionals carved out of native stone, additional advantages would accrue. The native practitioners would be more likely to remain in the areas from which they were recruited and form a continuous underpinning of primary care. In a large measure they would share the life-style of their patients; they could communicate more effectively; they would be more likely to influence the system towards changes which would be acceptable to the patients.

A corps of such practitioners would not remove the need for physicians, but it would change their role and reduce the demand to a quantity more like the supply. We have already begun to take a few faltering steps in this direction. A generation or two ago no self-respecting physician would have let his nurse give an injection. Today we are developing nurse-practitioners and the like. At the same time computers can synthesize the highest state of the medical art in such matters as diagnosis or therapy and make the knowledge available to all practitioners. The physician monitors the disease process, but we are rediscovering the patient as distinct from the disease.

Our interest in physicians' assistants reflects our recognition that modern medicine includes the concept of trade-offs and alternatives. Comprehensive care cannot be effectively translated into a specialist in every center. There is no magic formula or fixed recipe of services for a given population base. In an era when we realize we know so little about optimum care, much is to be gained by allowing service units to pursue a variety of approaches, *if* we insist upon an evaluation of each approach in terms of efficiency and effectiveness. Too often the federal system has sought for *the* approach with the result emerging as the lowest common denominator. By encouraging an atmosphere of experimentation and evaluation, and administrator is most likely to get the best from his staff.

Creative programming will call for creative funding—and here the Indian Health Service points up the hazard of getting caught in the numbers game. We have too long witnessed the effects of starvation on programs as well as people. New programs are bred at a time when politicians and bureaucrats are struggling frantically to make the old ones work. Ongoing care programs require increasing annual support, but nothing loses congressional interest like more of the mundane for the minorities. We hope that any future programs will be funded on the basis of need, perhaps by some system of capitation which is weighted to allow for regional differences in geography, economy, and health levels. In addition, incentives should be incorporated which reward the local units for efficiency and good management. Savings should be available for extras rather than refunded into the national treasury. From experience we know the frustration of saving money in one department and being unable to spend it for badly needed hospital supplies. After a time good management begins to seem rather pointless.

But is it really practical to write of rational solutions to a problem like health care for the poor? Moynihan and others suggest that such questions of national policy are more political than professional. The programs that emerge are more likely to meet the needs of pressure groups than those of professors. In Shiprock, we have already learned the frustration of trying to develop even the most unsophisticated priority index, and the greater frustration of trying to act on ordered priorities. Can we expect that a national index would be more readily accepted? How many people are prepared to abandon the old methods, however unsatisfactory, to risk a new method of health care delivery, however rational? What organized professional body will step aside or lend a hand to develop a system which may threaten its power base?

If indeed, the decisions are political, we may be speculating with impunity, confident that our theories can never be put to the test. On the other hand, we suspect that the political factors can be influenced by the growing dissatisfaction of the consumers. Soon the public will be ready to support a program which is not more of the same. The medical professions could try to insert a new formula with an old name, or they could be ready with some genuine innovations based on past experiences.

REFERENCES

1. Kennedy, E. *Congressional Record*, July 21, 1970.
2. Magnuson, W. *Congressional Record*, July 21, 1970.
3. Carter, L. J. Rural health: OEO launches bold Mississippi project. *Science*, 1967, *156*, 1466-58.
4. Kennedy, *op. cit.*

Chapter XIII
Conclusion: The End Result

COMMUNITY MEDICINE IN PRACTICE

The experience described in the foregoing chapters reflects the community medicine background and philosophy of the authors. The story of this interaction with the Indian Health Service represents a case study in the application of a community medicine approach to the real-world problems encountered in a comprehensive health care system. However, some amplification seems necessary on just what we mean by the term "community medicine."

Community medicine, as a distinct discipline and medical school department, has existed in the United States for less than a decade. Yet the concept of community medicine, as we define it, appeared in medical literature much earlier. We have no wish to trace the complicated history of the idea which is giving birth to an increasing number of community medicine departments in medical schools across the country. But we do note that, as community medicine has taken its place among related terms such as public health, preventive medicine, and social medicine, semantic confusion has ensued. Not only do freshmen in medical schools have difficulty in defining the terms, but rarely do two faculty members in a community medicine department define their discipline in exactly the same way.

Necessarily, then, the definition we offer is simply the one we have accepted. For us, community medicine is the identification of health problems in communities and the search for solutions to these problems.* Community medicine looks further than to the direct programs that meet immediate demands for service placed on an institution. It attempts to find alternative ways to decrease morbidity and improve health. This might include identifying

---

* This is not exclusively our definition. See Tapp, J. W. and Deuschle, K. W., The Community Medicine Clerkship: A Guide for Teachers and Students of Community Medicine, *Milbank Mem. Fund Quart.* 47: 411-47, October, 1969 (Part I).

groups that do not currently utilize health care, thus increasing the load on a facility rather than relieving it. The community medicine approach might identify health problems which had previously been considered outside of the health sphere. In community medicine, the focus is on the entire community to be served; the end point is improved community health, and the whole delivery system, however elaborate, is a means to that end. The perpetuation or aggrandizement of the delivery system cannot be an end in itself.

Since communities are always in a state of flux, community medicine is, above all, a dynamic process. The analytic skills involved in community diagnosis are borrowed from a variety of disciplines, each of which boasts a definite body of knowledge, but there is no collection of accumulated wisdom which provides the "right answers" for solving a given community's health problems. Community medicine, rather, provides tools and a state of mind for the ongoing process of evaluating and re-evaluating the status of a community's health and the instruments which try to improve that status. Perhaps this dynamic quality is the feature which most separates community medicine from public health, which is generally regarded as a body of knowledge and a career category as opposed to a process.

Community medicine is, and must be, interdisciplinary. Physicians, nurses, anthropologists, sociologists, nutritionists, social workers, statisticians, and environmentalists are some of the professionals who may be found in the various departments of community medicine. As time goes on, other disciplines will surely be added.

We hoped we could examine the health problems of our given Navajo community from the vantage point of community medicine, and even seek new solutions. In this battle, allies were essential. The staff of the Service Unit was engaged in direct service, and nobody's time was structured to allow for leisurely consideration of his impact on community health. Our goal was not to turn each employee into a community medicine specialist, but to foster a milieu in which staff members could feel that they were part of an evolving effort to meet ever-changing community health problems. We hoped that personnel would stop thinking of their job descriptions and start thinking of the job to be done.

Attitudes Towards Change

The community medicine approach called for involvement of the Service Unit personnel; yet the hierarchical organization of the Indian Health Service, as we have seen in Chapter III, tended to reward conformity and punish initiative. Furthermore, the patients and potential patients living in the community needed to be involved in the examination of health problems and the choice of solutions. But the history of the relationship between Anglo providers and Navajo consumers, described in Chapter II, made this kind of working alliance quite improbable.

We have indicated that the Indian Health Service careerists were caught in an organizational system which encouraged passivity and frustrated ambition. Change, to them, became a commodity handed down from above. This attitude is not unique to the Indian Health Service. Any massive medical care organization must create a large career force and provide some assurance of job security, benefits, and regular promotions to its members. Even in the private sector the dilemma presents itself; how does one provide secure and fair personnel practices within a large organization, often geographically dispersed, without making the individuals feel like mere cogs in a well-oiled machine?

From the top of a large organization, a message filters down suggesting behavior for staff members that will be most rewarded. Quoting from a Public Health Service training manual in an earlier chapter, we indicated that the Indian Health Service chooses "loyalty" as the most important attribute of its employees. Such choices should be conscious decisions since each quality sought brings a host of others in its train. The loyal employee is probably the unquestioning employee. The community medicine approach to health problems must begin and end with an enormous question mark.

The change-seeking spirit can be inculcated at the local level of a single hospital or health outpost, even in a hierarchy which seems to discourage innovation. The process of seeking change in Shiprock was described in detail in Chapter VII ("A Service Unit in Search of a Program"). That account is a documentation of the trial-and-error method in a medical setting. In the course of one year, some ideas led to successful new programs, others proved unworkable in practice, and still others remained fond imaginings. The important fact was that suggestions began to emanate from all departments of the organization. Employees showed a willingness to look at themselves critically (for example, the self-auditing program of physicians and the time-efficiency analysis of visiting nurses), which is a first step towards change. From this experience, we have emerged with a tentative recipe for producing an atmosphere conducive to innovation. Our recipe has four basic ingredients:

1. *Belief in Change.* Change must seem possible, and employees must

believe that they have power to influence its direction. This attitude—really a "suspension of disbelief" in change—can evolve when employees are asked for opinions, when they are placed on committees according to their expressed interests, or when they are asked to develop a personal idea further and put it into writing. Most of all, a belief in the possibility of change comes through observation of changes already put into effect on the suggestion of a fellow staff member.

"Belief in change" involves more than a sense that change is possible. Staff members must also believe in change as something desirable. To some health employees, change has been a mere nuisance—it has meant learning new routines and filling out new forms. The lower level employees rarely have a sense of the meaning of change in terms of the total program. As for middle-level administrators and professionals, we have noted that in the Indian Health Service they tend to fear innovation and the interloping two-year men who suggest it. Local health officials know that change which works out poorly requires a scapegoat. Therefore, they cling to the *status quo* as a security blanket. The safest course for the conditioned employee is to wait until a change is ordered from above, preferably sanctioned by an instruction manual on its implementation. Nonetheless, a local Service Unit has several advantages as an initiator of change. Local experimentation can be relatively inexpensive and it will be more responsive to regional needs. The success or failure of locally sponsored changes can serve as a guideline to the total organization.

To help personnel on a local level believe in the desirability of change, the local administrator and the various department heads must make certain that staff members are rewarded for trying a new approach and not penalized for the failure of an attempt.

2. *Delegated Authority.* Employees feel committed to the search for new approaches when they are offered real responsibility. True authority should be delegated to the heads of various departments such as nursing, environmental health, field health, pharmacy, health education, and so on. Even the right to make mistakes must be delegated. Robert Townsend makes this point in his *Up the Organization,* which addresses itself largely to the management of big industries and profit-making firms. It is easy to forget that a health organization can also be a large industry and could profit by some of the maxims of good management which encourage creative pursuit of the company's goals.

3. *Recognition.* We have already pointed out that the Public Health Service does not allow its local administrators and department heads very much latitude in rewarding employees. Promotions and special privileges tend to be rather automatic. With such constrictions, ingenuity is required to find ways of recognizing creative efforts. Luckily, verbal recognition is a more potent tool than is generally acknowledged, and does not add a cent to the budget.

4. *Research.* Finally, the impetus for change is closely linked to practice-oriented research within an organization. When employees raise questions, the astute administrator responds by wondering, "Is there any way we can study this?" Grumbling, which seems a constant activity among health employees, can be channelled constructively into demonstration projects which experiment with alternative methods. Chapter IX discusses the many possibilities for research within the local units of a federal health program. We should re-emphasize here that affiliation with professional health schools and the presence of students from the various health disciplines stimulates a questioning stance in permanent employees and provides manpower which makes research feasible.

Funding

The skeptic may wonder if a new orientation towards change will make an appreciable difference in the effectiveness of federal programs which are so chronically underfunded. It could be argued that, no matter how inventive the local employees, the task is one of making a silk purse out of a sow's ear. We admit to the shortage of money within the Indian Health Service and realize that some of the efforts described in this monograph were aimed at bringing more health money into our community. But the need for money can obscure an important point about funding. The manner in which funds are administered is as important as the amount allocated.

A lack of money is too often assumed to be the root of all evil in the public medical care system. Critics castigate their favorite villain, whether it be the "hospital corporate state," the "medical-industrial complex," the American Medical Association, or, perhaps, the insensitive legislators who are not willing to vote sufficient funds to public medical programs. The assumption, seemingly, is that America's health problems would be solved with the establishment of a viable financial base. We disagree.

Our experience with the Indian Health Service suggests that the difficulties in rendering modern medical care cannot be measured in dollars and cents alone. Certainly the Indian Health Service is one of the "underprivileged" among medical systems. Just as individuals in poverty are often burdened with large, problem-ridden families, medical institutions in poverty seem to serve the largest populations with the worst health conditions. Few poor men scorn to become rich, and, accordingly, many hospitals and medical organizations spend a disproportionate amount of time plotting get-rich-quick schemes. Unfortunately a medical care system could contrive to make its budgetary dreams come true and still fail to provide effective care!

The manner of funding, as well as the amount, has an observable effect on the philosophical outlook of the organization. For some time to come, funding will be a major determinant of activity. Put more succinctly, he who pays the piper calls the tune! A financial base which is arbitrarily fixed with no relationship to workload, program effectiveness, or local need (and no flexibility to rise to an occasion) lays the groundwork for the discouragement which can pervade a system. A mythology quickly develops around the whimsical deities who allocate funds. We have seen this phenomenon in the Indian Health Service, where bureaucratic mandarins have reverted to mystical rites of conformity and the innovators who challenge the system are considered heretics. Like most heretics, they tend to be sacrificed.

Current economic philosophy seems to favor some form of capitation payment for health care as a means of controlling costs. Yet to this must be added incentives to foster innovation over and above productivity. A plan which rewards productivity alone conjures up images of the work-quotas and overproduction of a socialist system. In practice, the quota system has a hidden pitfall. Since criteria based on past performance needs to be exceeded in subsequent years, prudence suggests unexacting measures to begin with. Such a policy could work to retard production rather than enhance it. As for innovation, it has little place in so closely monitored a set-up.

One gamut to avoid a self-defeating quota system is outright competition between institutions. The productivity of an agency is then matched against that of similar agencies. This type of competition also fosters a reliance on numbers, the so-called "hard data." Reporting can become equivalent to producing. Administrators mobilize all available energy and ingenuity to enhance their statistics. In the end, the same demons that plague the fee-for-service system emerge; the premium is on ill-health and inefficiency, for the more often a patient is seen the more swollen become the service statistics.

This quandary could be avoided by a refocusing of evelution away from services rendered. Instead, the actual effects of medical and health services must be evaluated. Funding should bear a direct relationship to genuine productivity as measured by end results. Those who allocate funds, of course, must make allowances for the fact that a given end result may be easier to achieve in some populations than in others. Generally speaking, health programs aimed at indigent groups (whose health status tends to be poor) or at rural groups (whose dispersion over a wide area makes the deployment of personnel necessarily inefficient) are likely to be more expensive than programs aimed at a population with fewer problems. If funding were thus directly tied in with goal-oriented program planning, hospitals and health services would be forced to examine their activities critically. Although such a necessity would probably be anxiety-provoking, the need for end-result evaluation is indisputable.

End-Result Evaluation

What do we mean by end-result evaluation? Simply stated, it is a process of setting program goals in terms of desirable effects on the health of the community being served. Periodic measurements of community health status are required to determine whether the goals are being realized. The desired health goal must never be an enlargement of the health mechanism itself; an agency should not point with pride to a new facility, additional personnel, or a heavy clinic load unless this circumstance has had a positive effect on the health of the consumer population. Often an assumption is made by health providers and consumers alike that an addition to a hospital must be a good thing *per se* for the community's health. Such an assumption could only be supported by solid evidence comparing the health status of the community before and after the hospital addition.

End-result evaluation can be applied by a clinician assessing the results of his interventions on the individual patient. The important fact is not the number of clinic visits made by the patient or the number of procedures performed on him. The central fact is not even the correctness of the diagnosis. What really matters is the actual effect which the health services have had on the patient's well-being. To make such an evaluation, one would require a clear understanding of the patient's degree of disability and discomfort before treatment as well as after.

In the community sphere, end-result evaluation utilizes the same principle as for an individual patient. When evaluating a community program, however, a critic can become dazzled by a display of facilities and a proliferation of programs. Yet it is the effectiveness of a health program which must be measured, not its size or good intentions. To measure effectiveness, a variety of tools must be found to measure the actual health status of a community.

Yardsticks to measure community health are hard to find. Clearly concentration on end results is more difficult than counting heads and procedures. Good health is a commodity which is hard to define, let alone measure. Usually we fall back on measurements of disease, and even then we have difficulties. Mortality figures are the most obvious index of community health—such measurements as life expectancy and infant mortality are fairly accurate throughout the whole country. When these crude indices are used to look at our Shiprock community, it is apparent that the health effort is not designed to combat one of the leading causes of death, namely, accidents.

When we try to measure other signs of ill-health which are less decisive than death we run into more difficulty. We cannot measure the incidence of ill-health in a community by counting hospitalizations or visits to a doctor; many factors influence whether an illness is treated, including the personal beliefs of the sick person and the accessibility of treatment. Sometimes the most serious symptoms are not brought to medical attention. Another way of measuring health status is to look at the level of functioning among adults in a community in terms of employment levels and utilization of sick leave. A region such as the Navajo reservation, however, does not offer full employment even to its healthy residents. Furthermore, the Navajo culture does not place the same positive value on work as does the Anglo culture. In Chapter VIII we discuss an attempt to measure the effects of treatment of some common diseases often seen on the reservation. The attempt floundered; the physicians who had dealt with the problems for years were very reluctant even to estimate how the diseases, in their treated and untreated states, affected levels of discomfort and disability in the patients.

End-result evaluation is a sensitive matter; it questions the actual relationship between medical care and health status. Socio-biological philosophers, among them René Dubos, have long insisted that the reduction of morbidity and mortality is more the result of social, economic, and environmental change than the availability of medical care or even than the advances in medical science. Reduction in specific disease states, they insist, has repeatedly preceded the specific scientific breakthrough, be it miracle drug or vaccine.

Some medical specialties are luckier than others in their ability to link professional activities to a definite beneficial result in the patient's health. For example, the orthopedic surgeon can usually be confident that his medical intervention will leave the patient in better condition than if the injury had been left untreated. Similarly, antibiotic treatment of infectious disease can change the outcome from possible death, if untreated, to possible complete recovery, if treated. Physicians, unfortunately are increasingly called upon to treat chronic diseases and problems with psychosomatic components. In these situations, the beneficial results of treatment are not so dramatic or so well understood. In Chapter VI (Infection and Affliction), we suggest that even in the Shiprock area, where infectious disease and traumatic injuries are certainly present, the hospital and clinics have been increasingly presented with chronic problems. In such instances, the health personnel are challenged by the need to help the patient cope with a longterm condition; they are assigned the very difficult task of bringing about behavioral changes in the patient which will allow him to adapt to his condition.

End-result evaluation becomes even more crucial in considering the effectiveness of treatment of patients with chronic problems. We suspect that, in many instances, expectations of the medical care system will have to be narrowed to the alleviation of discomfort and the improvement of function. This goal does not diminish the importance of the health professionals. Rather it engages them in the very difficult task of refining techniques of producing behavioral changes, of ensuring that patients are motivated to follow medical regimens, and of involving the patient as an active participant in the preservation of his own health. As a starting point, health professionals need to break down the components of medical intervention that do satisfy the patient and make a positive impact on his physical or mental well-being.

Part of the data for analyzing the doctor-patient relationships and their actual effectiveness in promoting physical or mental health must come from the patients themselves. End-result evaluation cannot confine itself to the activities in the doctor's office or the hospital ward. In Chapter V, we reported an opinion survey of Navajo patients in the Shiprock Area. Some of the responses suggested that a visit to the hospital left the patient anxious or humiliated. Other responses indicated that certain patients who tired of waiting at the clinic simply left without the medicines required for maintenance of their health status. Unlike laboratory data, this kind of human response information is hard to collect, hard to analyze, and hard to utilize, but it is, nonetheless, important in considering the effectiveness of the medical care which is offered.

We would make one further point about end-result evaluation. If this outlook ever became the predominant mode of thinking in medical organizations, the dichotomy between curative and preventive efforts in the health field should disappear. In Chapter VII, our description of the actual program at Shiprock dwells on the lack of understanding, communication, and sympathy between those in the clinical services and those in the field health unit, which administered the preventive health programs. In discussing the implications for a National Health Corps, in Chapter XII, the issue recurs. There we emphasize the need for a clear understanding of whether the National Health Corps should and could involve itself in preventive programs which would possibly plunge the Corps headlong into politics. Our concept of end-result evaluation, however, fantasizes a situation in which all those rendering health care are conditioned towards the goal of improved community health. Under these circumstances, a sharp distinction between the curative and the preventive would be impossible to maintain.

We have recommended that, in a centralized system of direct medical care, the funding of the various units should be based on the necessities of an effective program. Our foregoing discussion, however, points up the still unmet need to develop measurements for an effective health program. Obviously this step must come first. Perhaps the energies of the central organization, for example, the headquarters of the Indian Health Service in Washington, should be diverted to the stimulation of research which will suggest ways of evaluating actual program effectiveness in terms of improvement in the health status of the communities being served.

Centralization and Morale

Our case example of a local service unit on the Navajo reservation illustrates some of the problems in the service level of a large, decentralized health organization. At the forefront of these problems was the sense of discouragement which seemed to pervade the thinking of all the persons associated with the effort.

As the United States moves closer to health insurance in one form or another, further centralization of health care administrations seems inevitable. Even if the federal government chooses to underwrite the costs of health care which is purchased from third-party vendors (such as the Medicare program), some central controls will be necessary to maintain a uniform quality of services. Only by some degree of centralization can minimum standards of care be assured. We would hope that centralization does not have to be synonymous with demoralization.

The Indian Health Service has shown us that enthusiasm and energy are scarce commodities in an organization which does not provide incentives for performance. The individual employee has few personal incentives towards excellence, and the Service Units, as collective entities, are as likely to be penalized as rewarded for displays of increased efficiency or effectiveness. In such a setting, funded by rigid rules and characterized by vaguely-defined, unsatisfactorily-realized human relationships, the institutions become demoralized, the individual administrators and professionals become demoralized, and the patients themselves become demoralized.

If our story has a moral, it is simply that good medical care cannot exist in a demoralized atmosphere. With apologies to Marshall McLuhan, "the morale is the moral." A medical system cannot hope to rise above the spirits of the persons treating and treated within it.

Health services have become a complex operation, and the inter-relationships of the various individuals involved in health care are notoriously strained in almost all settings. The growing centralization of health care merely exacerbates the issues. Adjustments must be made, not only horizontally to relate to the various disciplines involved in health care and health planning, but also vertically to ensure good communications on the various levels of a health hierarchy. In the Indian Health Service, we observed a sense of impotence at each rung of the organizational ladder, among all disciplines involved in the team effort, and, regrettably, among the patients, who were passive recipients of care.

A need exists to restructure the human relationships which seem to operate so painfully within a medical hierarchy. Specifically, we want to touch on three questions which the Navajo experience raised for us:

1. How can dealings between a central administration and local administrations in its jurisdiction be restructured on a basis of mutual respect and benefit?

2. How can relationships between administrators, physicians, and other proliferating health professionals be restructured to enhance communication and reduce misunderstandings and tensions?

3. How can consumers be admitted to the inner circle of planners in a capacity which will facilitate their active and productive participation without jeopardizing their confidence in health professionals when they are in the patient role?

RELATIONSHIP BETWEEN LOCAL ADMINISTRATIONS AND
CENTRAL AUTHORITY

In any centralized system of medical care, whether it be a State Health
Department program made up of local departments, a system of hospitals
privately financed on a prepayment basis, or a federal program like the Indian
Health Service, which provides complete care to a category of patients,
minimum standards must be set for the organization. The central staff are
responsible for promoting overall efficiency and effectiveness, while maintaining minimum standards of care for all patients at all locations. The local
administrators are responsible for seeking maximum excellence for the constituency they serve. The large systems, such as the Indian Health Service, have
created middle-level offices responsible for maintaining the balance between
the goals of headquarters and the goals of the local Service Units. Theoretically, the existence of these regional offices keeps the organization in tune
with the variations in local needs. As our description of the Area offices of
the Indian Health Service in Chapter VIII suggests, the bureaucratic cadres
created to oversee various regions and subregions tend to impede rather than
enhance the balanced operation of the whole program.

Caught between a pressure from above to maintain standards of services
and reporting, and a pressure from below for flexibility and responsiveness,
the various intermediate level offices respond to conflicting gravitational pulls
with immobility. Not surprisingly, bureaucracies have been compared to
cancers, which, in their growth, deplete the vital energies of the total
organism, and, if allowed to grow unchecked, eventually consume it.

Management has not found the cure for bureaucratic cancer. But a
counterattack lies in strategic selection of personnel to staff the upper
echelons of the hierarchies. These appointees should be selected from proven
problem-solvers at the local levels. Regional offices should not become
respositories of incompetence. Rather they should be sources for creative
consultations, a process which is goal-directed and concerned with suggesting
alternative means of achieving local aims. The regional offices should be adept
at helping local personnel redefine problems when necessary to facilitate more
productive approaches.

Too much administrative apparatus decidedly hampers creative programs
at a local level. A severe means test must be applied to the organizational
structure itself; either an office serves a real function acknowledged by those
above and below, or that office is abolished!

Perhaps the demoralization within the administrative structure is a bow to political necessity. As a public program, the Indian Health Service at all levels tried to avoid antagonizing any powerful interests. The dependency on Congressional appropriations was a great immobilizing agent, making the agency avoid controversy at all costs to effectiveness. We have seen that the effort of the Shiprock agency to impose quality standards in the care which it purchased from surrounding towns was deemed too dangerous to continue. We have also noted that the Indian Health Service on the Navajo reservation was not willing to take any position on the important health issue of whether liquor should be legalized on the reservation. An agency which avoids anything controversial may have a longer life expectancy, but at a considerable sacrifice. It abrogates its role as health spokesman and ceases to be an advocate of the population it is serving. Eventually the feeling of impotence takes hold, for an agency which is afraid to take any risks really is powerless to change an undesirable situation.

The fear of antagonizing the white community or private medical interests is present at all levels of the Indian Health Service structure, from the Service Units, through the Areas, all the way to headquarters. The correction has to be applied from the top of the hierarchy so that local and regional officials know that they will receive top level support for any defensible stands taken on health issues.

RELATIONSHIPS BETWEEN VARIOUS HEALTH DISCIPLINES

Beyond the difficulties between local and central authorities, a second area of conflict that dissipates the creativity of a working health unit is the troubled relationships prevailing among the various health professionals. It would seem that the different groups feel that their particular interests are threatened by true teamwork—that is, a coordinated effort toward a common goal. Yet professional feathers can remain unruffled and professional pride inspired when expertise is channelled into its appropriate arenas.

The skillful administrator is the individual who should be expected to bring about this harmony. The various health professionals involved in direct service, however, usually are in accord on one point; they do not like administrators very much. Too often the latter is type-cast as the villain who announces shortages of funds or the need for belt-tightening. He is seen as the impediment to change who cites regulations, precedents, or possible consequences which should be considered. There are administrators who fit the stereotype, especially in a hierarchical organization where the administrator's actions really are somewhat constricted.

It is ironical that the image of the administrator has become so opposite to what we consider his correct function. In Chapter XI, we discuss the question of whether an administrator should be a physician, concluding that formal background may be varied as long as the administrator is equipped with the necessary perspective and knowledge to function effectively in his role. Ideally that role should be that of the facilitator—the expert in finding ways to get things done and make things happen. A reconciliation between administrators and the direct service part of a medical staff can only be based on respect for what the administrator can achieve.

Perhaps as evaluation of health care shifts from measurements of the process to actual end-result evaluation of effectiveness in the community, the administrator will be in a more potent position to exercise leadership. The extent to which the whole institution can formulate and share goals for community health will reflect the skill of the administrator. Given a desired outcome, he should be able to work with the appropriate professional groups to develop approaches most conducive to the goals sought. In this way a team is forged in which each professional group has a part in reaching for a projected goal.

Of all professionals, the physician is the hardest to channel. The training of a doctor seems to create a sense of omnipotence which transcends professional boundaries. The doctor typically regards himself as capable of performing most tasks, perhaps with a little additional training. With this attitude, he tends to view associates as subordinates. His own activities are paramount—the importance of the efforts of others depends upon the degree to which they augment his own services.

Several factors contribute to this personality pattern.* The doctor does perform a socially valued role, well rewarded with money and prestige. Throughout his training, and to some extent in his professional life, his present and future actions are inputed to affect a life-or-death outcome. Defense mechanisms are necessary under such stress. The favorite defense mechanisms seem to be feelings of infallibility and projection of guilt. Unfortunately, these protective maneuvers produce attitudes which are demoralizing to the other groups who must work with the doctor in rendering modern health care.

Logically, one could argue that other nonmedical occuaptions, such as

---

* See two books by Eliot Freidson. *Profession of Medicine: A Study of Applied Knowledge* (Dodd, Mead & Co; New York, 1970) and *Professional Dominance: The Social Structure of Medical Care* (Atherton; New York, 1970).

automobile mechanic or airline pilot, call for at least as many small decisions with life-and-death implications as does medicine. More often than not, it is difficult to draw a causal relationship between many of the physician's actions and the eventual health status of the patient. Still, the doctor has captured the public imagination; as half a dozen television series attest, he is depicted as the hero of a dramatic race against the ravages of disease.

It is not accidental that the physician (rather than, for instance, the garage mechanic) is blown into such heroic proportions by the public that he has begun to believe his own legend. Doctors are present during the mysterious human crises of birth and death. As the heirs of the medicine men and priests of other societies, physicians serve an important ritualistic function.

The present mystique of medical practice has developed out of the scientific revolution. Computers and molecular formulae have replaced ceremonies and incantations. Still the mystical curtain which separates the professional and the layman, allowing us to open our psychic and physical privacies to inspection and manipulation, remains an important relic of earlier times. Thus the language and equipment of science serves the "unscientific" function of surrounding the doctor in the aura of mystery appropriate to solemn life moments.

We are saying, then, that the physician is hard to channel for a variety of reasons, but one of the reasons is that he occupies a symbolic role dictated by the larger society which produces him. In the end, the choice rests to a large extent with society itself. If it highly values the sanctity of the profession with the emotional support that view provides, it must accept the side-effects as well. On the other hand, if the public resents its inability to participate in decision-making, it must be willing to forsake some of the solace the present professional posture provides.

The fact that the scientific trappings of modern medicine have taken on a ritualistic quality is more apparent in a setting such as the Navajo reservation where the patients have not abandoned their own symbolism regarding birth and death. The impersonal quality of a hospitalization, instead of seeming like the orderly and correct ceremony at a time of illness, is perceived as neglect and disinterest by the less acculturated Navajo patients.

In any event, the professional posture of the physician increases the distance between himself and those colleagues who should be his allies. At the same time, it increases the insecurity and sense of inferiority of other disciplines around him. As we have seen in Chapter III, the personnel pattern in the Indian Health Service exacerbated this problem. The physicians tended to be the conscripted two-year men who were young, liberal, impatient, and fresh from the training that produced the attitudes we have just described. Moreover, they had no permanent roots in the community.

Health administrators have long recognized the futility of direct confrontation with physicians. Too often, however, they have resorted to the opposite posture of passivity and pacification. Rather, they should seek an alliance with the physicians toward a common goal. In this effort they might take advantage of some of the prototypic physician personality characteristics which cannot easily be changed.

Physicians usually are pragmatic people. They are accustomed to relatively immediate rewards for their actions in terms of patient improvement or gratitude. If goals were redefined towards community health, physicians would have to realize that their success depended in part on the skills of other disciplines.

Of course, no instantaneous transformation of ingrained professional values of physicians can be expected. This gradual process can come about best through change in focus in medical education. But some progress is possible when the administrator recognizes the problem and is willing to play a dynamic role.

RELATIONSHIPS BETWEEN CONSUMERS AND PROVIDERS

Finally, the patients themselves constitute the group that may be most demoralized by the medical care systems which serve them. At the same time as the public is endowing the medical establishment with a certain glamor, complaints abound that medical care is expensive, time-consuming, inefficient, depersonalized, and confusing. The patient believes in the scientific miracles of transplants, and he also believes in the dedication of the hard-working family physician. But somehow the wonders of science and the wisdom of the friendly, concerned doctor do not seem readily available to him when he needs them. For many of us, the medical care system is yet another product which cannot live up to its advertised claims. Every daily paper reports human interest stories of modern medical miracles; this merely increases the frustrations of the patients when their own experiences with medical treatment prove so unsatisfying.

Further pressure is heaped on the patient-consumer. The concept of consumer representation on health boards has received growing acceptance. Now the patient is expected to relate to the medical establishment in a dependent, trustful position during personal illness, and as an informed critic when he serves as consumer representative to policy-making groups. This dual role has been awkward and threatening for both the consumer and the provider.

The current health care system appears to many as a fortuitous concourse of independent parts. Decisions are made on the basis of insufficient information and often for the wrong reasons. But the transfer of that incompetence in health planning to a new faction offers little advantage. Consumers catapulted into the role of policy-makers invariably come into conflict with professionals eager to defend their turf. Expertise and jargon become professional weapons to fend off invaders. In a recent discussion, Dr. George Silver has recognized this problem:

> Clearly, patients have been marked as non-starters in the leadership race. The fact is only one expression of the crucial and growing role of the expert in our society. He is beginning to take over, along with his computers, technologically complicated inventions, and esoteric knowledge. We don't want him to take over—we want to use him—but we are at his mercy, because he has information that he jealously guards. Medical practice offers a paradigm of this dilemma, and, however the new laws are written, it will obviously be difficult to keep the doctors in line, to lessen their control over the nature and quality of their work and its application (1).

Essentially the health workers are wrapping themselves up in professionalism to avoid a planning alliance with patients. But the consumers sometimes retaliate by insisting on their rights to control the health machine. Numerous examples spring to mind, especially from highly politicized urban ghetto areas such as Harlem, Bedford-Stuyvesant, or Watts. One thinks of the siege of Lincoln Hospital in the Bronx by the Young Lords, or the pressure placed on the Neighborhood Health Center at Columbia Point in Boston. The latter is a multi-faceted service program located in a large public housing development which found itself embarrassed by the efforts of the consumer board to take over management.*

Dr. Silver suggests better education of the consumers into the intricacies of the organization and delivery of health services. Another approach would be the development of a distinct role for consumers, assigning them the

---

* See Barbara and John Ehrenreich *The American Health Empire: Power, Profits, and Politics* (Vintage Books; New York, 1970), particularly Chapters XVI and XIX, for more examples of struggles between aroused communities and the health establishment.

responsibility for problem identification and, later, selection from a broad range of alternative solutions prepared by experts.

As an analogy outside of the medical sphere, a community group might quite appropriately define as a problem the difficulty in travelling within a city bisected by a river. After experts had developed feasibility data and engineers had been appointed to draw up actual plans, this same group might appropriately choose between various proposed sites and designs of tunnels and bridges. Presented with expert evidence, the community might decide that the cost of proposed solutions were prohibitive, or it might decide to go ahead with one of the plans. Note that, in this model of a procedure, the consumers are not mere figure-heads; they make decisions but they do not make technical plans.

This proposed responsibility for consumers would require a mechanism for tapping patient opinion. This could be accomplished by periodic community surveys or by an ongoing device to raise issues for consideration. (Municipal elections could serve as a means of measuring public feeling on health issues by plebescite; we would be wary of the election technique at the initial problem identification stage, but it might be helpful at the stage of choosing between alternatives.) Once health problems had been identified by the consumers, the providers, both professional and managerial, would be responsible for the development of alternative solutions together with an estimation of the cost and consequences of each choice.

In adopting this method, it is important to avoid a pitfall of many consumer-linked planning schemes. Too often problems are defined by one possible solution. Needs are expressed in terms of a deficit in facilities or personnel (for example, "We need a bigger hospital"). These problems are better dealt with if they are first expressed more descriptively. "We need a better hospital" is really just one solution to many problems ranging from "I have to wait too long for a bed" to "The wards are too crowded and uncomfortable" or "We have to drive to a bigger city to see a specialist." If the problem is expressed as a need for a new or bigger hospital, public opinion tends to crystallize around this particular solution before the problem is accurately defined. Too often more feasible alternatives are not considered when such a narrow definition of a problem is utilized. More flexibility in planning is possible if consumers first describe the problem in terms of their experiences with the health services.

Our Shiprock case study describes a community which was not politically activated to demand immediate consumer participation in the health agencies. Consumer demands on the system were in terms of a preconceived solution—a new addition to the hospital. Tribal officials had made the new addition a rallying cry at election time so that the public was aware of this particular proposal. For the most part, however, the typical consumer seemed to resemble those interviewed in our consumer study (reported in Chapter V). They were not entirely satisfied with the medical program of the Indian Health Service, would say so if asked, but did not perceive their role as participants in planning.

Tribal leaders, however, did consider themselves participants. In Chapter IV we have described various efforts on the part of tribal leaders to instruct the Service Unit director to chastise employees for their political persuasions. There was no convenient mechanism through which the Indian Health Service providers could speak directly to the Navajo consumers, by-passing the officials. We have described the newly created Health Advisory Board but pointed out that its membership consisted of elected tribal officials and their appointees. We have also discussed the problems encountered in our attempts to share the facts of the medical care program with the larger group of consumers.

Originally we had hoped to involve the community as an ally and impart to it factual information about the various services offered in the Service Unit facilities. We felt that potential patients should know the size of the budget, the utilization patterns of the hospital and clinics, and the size and distribution of the staff. This kind of openness may improve understanding between the provider and the consumer, but it can channel aggression elsewhere, usually to elected leaders. Probably for this reason the leaders in the Shiprock area were most reluctant to permit the Service Unit director to speak at meetings or distribute the fact booklet. This attitude would not be confined to a Navajo politican but would be expected to appear in other settings. As soon as constituents, anywhere, become appraised of the facts of their medical system, they may become convinced that health employees are doing the best they can under limiting circumstances. Then they turn to their elected leaders and make complaints. Anyone doubting that information is power should observe the careful way our politicans are monitoring the distribution of "Vietnam facts."

The tribal officials were willing, it seemed, to serve as health representatives on planning boards. But we have already raised the question of whether the experiences of an elite are ever sufficiently typical to make them adequate spokesmen for a community of patients.

Even when representatives of the typical patient are found, a question remains: how do the representatives stay representative? Experience with consumer boards suggests that the members can quickly take on the attributes and values of the providers. In other words, the increased responsibility causes these board members to identify more with the problems of the provider than with those of the consumer. An effort to educate the consumers who are named to health boards would only accelerate this process. Moreover, if the health establishment designed the education, it would be equivalent to the defendant briefing the jury on a point of law.

The prevalent American example of consumer participation in health care is the hospital board of trustees composed of the richest and/or most powerful men in the community. Such boards are by no means truly representative of the users of the hospital, but they are effective in securing funds and enforcing policies. In regions of poverty, the board members are generally upwardly mobile rather than established. Personal ambitions and power struggles can very easily become entangled with health issues. Even when less ambitious representatives can be found, their new positions of power in determining health policies might separate them from the ranks of their constituents. Indeed, this dilemma is inherent in the representative democracy which governs our nation. When tempted to despair over the difficulties in implementing consumer representation in the health field, we fall back on Winston Churchill's description of the democratic system itself. "Democracy," said Churchill in a speech in 1947, "is the worst form of government, except all those other forms which have been tried from time to time."

Our proposed approach would minimize some of these problems in finding a sufficiently representative board. Along with the board, there would also be continuous interaction with a broad base of consumers who would have a direct role in initiating changes by defining problems and choosing solutions. Finding the mechanisms for public expression might be difficult but it should not be impossible. In the Navajo Service Unit public opinion might be tapped through the community health representatives. Another approach would be utilization of the Chapter organizations which essentially are community-wide meetings. Most communities (especially those which are true communities in terms of background and common interests, rather than those established for the convenience of the government, which requires a reasonable population base for programs) will have existing formal and informal methods of communication which might be utilized for the exchange of feelings and information on health problems.

CONCLUSIONS

The generalizations of contemporary health planners and diagnosticians exhibit a fondness for pursuing an Aristotelian golden mean. They would like to see controls balanced by freedom of action. Consumer participation is integral, they say, but the provider role must not be threatened. Experimentation is vital, but service functions cannot be neglected. Health services must be centrally organized for long range planning and evaluation, but structural decentralization and preservation of individual initiative is necessary for consumer convenience and provider satisfaction.

This type of balance is a most elusive goal. The aspiration reminds us of the best thinking in child-rearing which cautions the parent to be neither too permissive nor too restrictive. In retrospect one can easily see when the scale is tipped to one side. But only instinct tells us how to balance the factors in practice. In health care, as in child-rearing, the imbalances become apparent only when the method has failed.

The balancing act is made more difficult by the fact that certain human characteristics are often combined. For example, a constellation of qualities such as action-orientation, willingness to change, ability to take initiative, and genuine concern with programs can predictably be united in one individual. In the same individual we can predict a certain recklessness, impatience, or even arrogance. We can only suggest that program planners and personnel managers make a conscious choice of direction, and make their emphasis known to potential recruits. We noted that, in the local units of the Indian Health Service, the careerists and the two-year men typically presented characteristics diametrically opposed to one another. Theoretically, a perfect balance was achieved. But when a scale is exactly balanced there is no motion. A program may be balanced into immobility.

Then too one must question the advisability of central planning balanced with decentralized operations. Some have argued that the separation of planning, evaluation, and policy-making from the delivery of health care is not feasible. We would suggest that the Indian Health Service experience bears out this contention. Innumerable local impediments stood in the way of centrally-declared goals.

It is said that everyone is in favor of progress but nobody wants to change. Yet change has become a part of the life experience of the current generation. Information is evolving at a logarithmic rate which far outstrips our capacity to digest it. One must marvel at the resistance to change evidenced by our institutions in the face of ever-changing information, but one cannot condone it.

Change means inconvenience, and each of us is reluctant to alter our fixed modes of behavior, no matter how great the potential growth. The extent to which the medical profession will resist change is illustrated by the following quotation from a respected newspaper:

That it will ever come into general use notwithstanding its value... *is* extremely doubtful; because its beneficial application requires much time and gives a good bit of trouble both to the patient and the practitioner; because its hue and character are foreign and opposed to all our habits and associations... There is something even ludicrous in the picture of a grave physician proudly listening through a long tube attached to the patient's thorax (2).

The date was 1834 and the writer was condemning the stethoscope!

In an atmosphere of tolerance to change, we must look to the past as well as to the future. As situations and settings are altered, old ideas may be revived and re-examined. We must seek to avoid the motto of the reactionary—"We tried that before and it didn't work."

We must also develop a respect for the new generation of health workers. In many instances old hands do not always know best. New tools for evaluation and management are developing, and new perspectives can shed light on horizons that habit has made hazy.

Throughout these pages we have sought to emphasize elements in the Indian Health Service's system which seemed to impede realization of the goals formally espoused. Perhaps foremost is the failure to recognize that the organization is not an inanimate object like the models we construct. It is made up of people who need support and gratification. Acknowledgement of both efforts and achievements must be a continued part of any organization, but it is most vital in a large bureaucracy in which the individual may have difficulty identifying his own personal role.

Using the Shiprock Service Unit as an example, we have tried to describe the workings of the Indian Health Service, demonstrating some of its strengths and weaknesses in its attempt to provide comprehensive health care. Unfortunately there is no facile formula to correct errors and place the organization on a sure path towards the goal of better health for the communities it serves.

There is, however, a tendency in the Indian Health Service to take action without examination of the rationale. Perhaps the long association with

Indians has encouraged the agency to say "how" instead of "why."

Asking "why" is crucial. Critical examination of the reasons for actions and an understanding of the effects which these actions have on the health of the community is the combination necessary to revitalize an agency like the Indian Health Service. We have seen that a transfusion of money will hardly make a dent in the problem; a transfusion of energy and sense of purpose is needed.

In this process, professional autonomy must bend to allow new relationships to emerge in the health complex. Administrators on all levels, health professionals of all kinds, and community residents must work together at defining goals and measuring the degree of success in reaching them. Otherwise a huge and complicated medical apparatus will rumble on without any agreement about where it is going or where it wants to go. Worse still, the cumbersome machine could spin its wheels and go nowhere, and both its drivers and its riders might not even notice.

REFERENCES

1. Silver, G. The patient as non-starter. *The Nation,* January 11, 1971, pp. 55-56.
2. *London Times,* 1834. Cited in V. A. McKusick, *Cardiovascular sound in health and disease.* Baltimore: The Williams and Wilkins Co., 1958.

Appendix A

Community Health Representative Questionnaire

Age _____ Male _____ Fe _____ Chapter _____

1. What are the most important health problems in your community? What can we do about them?

2. About what topics should there be health education? Who should give it?

3. What problems or difficulties have you had in getting help at the Shiprock Hospital or Clinic?

4. What other services would you like to be able to get at the Shiprock Hospital which are not available now?

5. Do you think that your community should have a Field Clinic? For what kind of problems would you use a Field Clinic?

Appendix B

Questionnaire for Study of Employee Opinion

NAVAJO AREA RESEARCH SURVEY

A. Please think for a moment about the following questions and give a brief answer. Use only brief phrases if you wish.

1. Is providing health care to Navajos different from providing care to other low income patients? If so, how?

2. Which one type of personnel is in the greatest shortage in the service units of the Navajo Area?

3. What changes could we make in our present activities to improve the health of the people the most?

4. What are the three most important health needs that are not now being adequately filled? (list only three).

5. If we have to reduce services due to a budget cut, which two of the following would you elminate? (circle appropriate letters).

    a. Dental Services
    b. Field clinics

c. General clinics (outpatient department)
d. Health education
e. Prenatal and well baby care
f. Inpatient care
g. Public Health nurses
h. Environmental health (sanitarian and sanitary engineer services)
i. Social services
j. Specialist services (ear surgery, contract care)

B. For each of the following statements, circle the letter which most closely indicates how you feel about that statement. Circle "a" if you agree fully, "b" if you agree partly, "c" if you feel neutral, "d" if you disagree mildly, and "e" if you disagree strongly.

6. The services provided by the Indian Health Service are an obligation of the U.S. government. a b c d e

7. The health care provided in the Navajo Area is better than the average health care available in the surrounding communities. a b c d e

8. The quality of health care provided by the PHS in the Navajo area is adequate. a b c d e

9. The Navajo Tribe should provide at least some of the health services that are currently provided by the PHS. a b c d e

10. The main reason for Navajos to have poor health is that they don't take care of themselves. a b c d e

11. There are certain health services which the individual Navajos should purchase for themselves instead of having the PHS provide them. a b c d e

12. The Navajo Area Service Units should   a b c d e
    charge a fee to those Navajos who can
    afford to pay.

13. The Navajo people should control the   a b c d e
    administration of health services on the
    reservation.

14. The Navajo Tribe gives full cooperation   a b c d e
    to the PHS.

15. The Navajo Tribe gives a high priority to   a b c d e
    health.

16. A national health insurance plan, like   a b c d e
    Medicare, but to all ages, should be
    adopted for the United States.

17. If a national health insurance plan were   a b c d e
    adopted, it should include the Indians.

18. If a national health insurance plan were   a b c d e
    adopted, the PHS should stop serving
    the Indians.

C. Of the following areas, indicate with an X which you consider to be the
    two most important to Navajo health. Next, indicate with an X the *two*
    areas needing the most *increase* in services.

		19. Most Important	20. Increase Needed
a.	Dental Services		
b.	Field clinics		
c.	General clinics (outpatient dept)		
d.	Health education		
e.	Prenatal and well baby care		
f.	Inpatient care		
g.	Public Health nurses		
h.	Environmental Health (sanitarian and sanitary engineer services)		
i.	Social services		
j.	Specialist services (ear surgery, contract care)		

D.   The following questions should be answered by selecting the answer which you feel is best and circling the number next to your choice. Remember that results are anonymous so just do the best you can. If you don't know the answer select the one you think is most likely to be correct.

21.   The population of the Navajo Area is close to—

    1)   50,000   3)   100,000
    2)   75,000   4)   150,000

22.   Most doctors in the Indian Health Service hospitals and clinics—

    1)   have not completed their medical degree
    2)   have completed their degree but have not specialized
    3)   are specialists
    4)   are former professors

23.   Navajo Area PHS hospitals will provide non-emergency direct care for—

    1)   any Navajo living on the reservation
    2)   any Navajo living in the service unit
    3)   any Navajo
    4)   any American citizen

24.   Half the population on the Navajo Reservation are below—

    1)   15 years of age   3)   25 years of age
    2)   20 years of age   4)   30 years of age

25.   For which of the following conditions is the Indian and Alaska Native death rate *lower* than the rest of the nation?

    1)   accidents
    2)   liver cirrhosis
    3)   cancer
    4)   tuberculosis

26. Which is *not* a function of the PHS here?

    1)   providing running water to homes
    2)   inspecting restaurants
    3)   providing electric power to homes
    4)   testing drinking water

27. Community Health Representatives are—

    1)   PHS employees   3)   BIA employees
    2)   Volunteers   4)   Navajo Tribe employees

28. The leading cause of hospital admissions for the Navajo Area is—

    1)   Accidents and injuries
    2)   Maternity (deliveries)
    3)   Diseases of the lungs (such as pneumonia and tuberculosis)
    4)   Diseases of the heart and circulation

29. Which service is not generally provided to patients?

    1)   False teeth
    2)   Immunizations
    3)   Physical exams
    4)   Eyeglasses for school children

30. Which figure in American history was most closely identified with the Navajos?

    1)   William Cody (Buffalo Bill)   3)   Wyatt Earp
    2)   General Custer   4)   Kit Carson

31. The Navajo language is most closely related to that of the—

    1)   Apache   3)   Maya
    2)   Hopi   4)   Shoshoni

32. The Navajos have lived on their present land for—

    1) longer than 1000 years
    2) between 400 and 1000 years
    3) between 150 and 400 years
    4) less than 150 years

33. A Sing lasts—

    1) several minutes   3) one month
    2) several days   4) over one month

34. The door of a hogan faces—

    1) North   3) East
    2) South   4) Any direction

35. The "Long Walk" was to—

    1) Fort Defiance   3) Tuba City
    2) Fort Laramie   4) Fort Sumner

36. A Navajo man belongs to the clan of his—

    1) Mother   3) Wife
    2) Father   4) Own choosing

37. "Crystal" may refer to—

    1) A type of ancient pottery
    2) A rug
    3) A doll
    4) A popular Navajo beverage

E. *Personal information.* Please choose the answer which most closely applies and circle the number next to it.

38. How much schooling have you had?

    1) Did not complete high school

2)   High school graduate
3)   Some college (or professional training)
4)   College graduate
5)   Beyond college

39. How many years have you been associated with the Navajo people?

1)   0-1 years   4)   5-10 years
2)   1-2 years   5)   over 10 years
3)   2-5 years

40. How many years have you been with the PHS?

1)   0-1 years   4)   5-10 years
2)   1-2 years   5)   over 10 years
3)   2-5 years

41. Which do you consider yourself?

1)   Navajo   3)   White
2)   Part Navajo   4)   Other

42. What is your age?

1)   below 21   4)   41-50
2)   21-30   5)   51-60
3)   31-40   6)   over 60

43. What is your sex?

1)   male   2)   female

44. What is your role in program planning for your service unit?

1)   Major role in overall planning
2)   Role in planning my specific area only
3)   Role in making suggestions to my superiors
4)   No role in program planning
5)   Never heard of program planning.

Glossary of Acronyms and Organizational Terms

Area Office:

The Indian Health Service is divided into ten Area offices dispersed throughout continental United States and Alaska. Each Area administers a number of Service Units across a broad geographic region. Although most Areas comprise several tribes, the Navajo Area office serves only the populous Navajo tribe (see IHS).

BIA

(Bureau of Indian Affairs) The BIA is an agency under the jurisdiction of the United States Department of the Interior. It has broad powers in the administration of Indian and Alaskan Native affairs on the reservations, including education, welfare, and land management programs. Since 1955, however, health programs have been removed from BIA responsibility.

Branch Chief

The branch chiefs administer the specific program categories in the Indian Health Service. In each Area office, there is usually a branch chief for maternal and child health, health education, environmental health, community health services, program planning, social work, dentistry, and nursing. The branch chief offers consultation in his particular program to the Service Units and reports to a corresponding branch chief at Indian Health Service headquarters.

Chapter

The local governments on the Navajo reservation are known as Chapters. In a system reminiscent of early American town meetings, all adults of a community participate in Chapter meetings conducted at a Chapter House and presided over by an elected president and vice-president. In addition, each

Chapter (or groups of smaller Chapters) elects a representative to the tribal council. Chapters vary in size; the Shiprock Service Unit, for example, contained 16 Chapters ranging in size from the large Shiprock Chapter to several very small Chapters.

COSTEP

(Commissioned Officer Student Training and Extern Program) This is a career development and recruitment program designed to give students in the health sciences practical experience with the PHS. Students in various disciplines serve as junior officers in assignments which inform them about the possibilities of a career with PHS.

CHR

(Community Health Representative) The CHR is a health worker who serves as a liason between members of his tribe and the Indian Health Service personnel. Although appointed by the various tribes, CHR's are paid by means of an Indian Health Service grant to the tribes. On some reservations, the CHR program is supported by Office of Economic Opportunity funds. The CHR is trained by the Indian Health Service, but responsible to his tribal leaders.

CMC

(Contract Medical Care) The Indian Health Service acts as a third party payee for medical care rendered to Indians and Alaskan Natives in other than its own facilities. Each Service Unit manages a CMC fund, designed primarily for emergency care away from Indian Health Service hospitals and for highly specialized treatment unavailable except at outside medical centers.

Commissioned Officer Corps

The Commissioned Officer Corps of the Public Health Service is a uniformed service in many respects on a par with the Army, Navy, and Air Force. Like the other branches of the services, the Corps is composed of some officers who are planning a life-time career in its membership and others who plan a limited stint in fulfillment of their military obligations (see PHS).

Cornell Project

The Cornell Project was a demonstration project resulting from an agreement between the Indian Health Service and Cornell Medical School. Staff from the school were authorized to conduct a multi-discipline pilot project on the Navajo reservation (at Many Farms, Arizona) to develop more effective methods of preventing and controlling tuberculosis among the Navajo.

DNA

(Dinebeiina Nahilna Be Agaditehe) DNA is the controversial legal aid program on the Navajo reservation that is funded through the Office of Economic Opportunity. The name of the organization may be translated roughly as "lawyers who work for the economic betterment of the people."

Field Health

The field health programs in the Indian Health Service are those preventive programs that are usually conducted by local public health departments in nonreservation communities. The activities include visiting nurse services, maternal and child health clinics, school health, immunization, and infectious disease control; field health is also referred to more descriptively as "community health services." The term "field health" is used rather than the familiar "public health" to prevent semantic confusion, since the whole operation is part of the United States Public Health Service.

Gallup

The Indian Health Service operates several hospitals that are designed as referral centers. In the Navajo Area, the major medical center is the Indian Health Service hospital at Gallup, New Mexico.

Headquarters

The Indian Health Service is administered centrally by a director with headquarters near Washington, D.C. (see IHS).

HEW

(Health, Education and Welfare) HEW is the agency of the federal government under which the Indian Health Service falls.

HPSC

(Health Programs Systems Center) HPSC is the health services research center operated by the Indian Health Service and located near Tuscon, Arizona.

HSMHA

(Health Services and Mental Health Administration) HSMHA is a division of HEW responsible for a wide variety of health programs including the Public Health Service hospitals, the Center for Disease Control, and a variety of grant programs in areas such as maternal and child health, family planning, mental health, comprehensive health planning, communicable diseases, etc. The Indian Health Service falls under this administration.

IHS

(Indian Health Service) The IHS is charged with the responsibility for programs related to the health of the Indians and Alaskan Natives, including direct curative services, preventive services and environmental surveillance. IHS is organized with headquarters in Washington and has ten Area offices throughout the country. Each Area directs one or more Service Units in its region. A Service Unit, the smallest jurisdiction in the IHS, may include a hospital, outpatient clinics, a field health unit, and a CMC fund.

OEO

(Office of Economic Opportunity) This federal agency, at its inception, administered a broad war on poverty, including Head Start, the Job Corps, and community action programs.

ONEO

(Office of Navajo Economic Opportunity) OEO funds expended on the Navajo reservation go through the tribe. Containing all the elements of an OEO program (see above), ONEO has been a source of employment and a training ground for administrators among the Navajo.

PHS

(Public Health Service) The PHS was an outgrowth of the Maritime Hospital system begun in the eighteenth century. Gradually a system evolved which offered direct health care for a variety of federal programs (such as the federal prisons, the Coast Guard, Indians and Alaskan Natives, federal narcotic patients) as well as more general programs to protect the nation's health (such as the National Institutes of Health and environmental control). The PHS Commissioned Officer Corps is organized as virtually a fourth branch of the military service with military ranks and benefits. In addition, PHS is manned by a civilian staff that conforms to Civil Service regulations. Since World War II, a two-year term of service in the PHS Officer Corps has been a legal alternative to military service for health professionals.

With recent reorganizations of the federal health system, many of the PHS components, including the Indian Health Service, fall under HSMHA in HEW. Recent trends suggest a disappearance of the concept of a Public Health Service *per se*, with the incorporation of its functions into a federal administrative structure.

Note: In this book, PHS has been used synonomously with IHS as was the custom on the reservation. In fact, many Navajo lumped all federal programs together in one word, "Washington."

PPBS

(Program Planning and Budgeting System) This is a system of planning originally developed by the Department of Defense. Local units develop objectives and programs to carry them out. These are synthesized into even larger programs at each level up the administrative hierarchy. Duplications are minimized and efficiency stressed. This technique was transiently applied to the federal health system in the mid 1960's.

Service Unit

This is the smallest administrative unit of the Indian Health Service (see IHS). Most of the examples in this book are drawn from the activities of a single Service Unit centered at Shiprock, New Mexico.

SUD

(Service Unit Director) The SUD is the Indian Health Service official (either commissioned officer or civil servant) who heads up the Service Unit and is responsible for its full scope of activities.

Tribal Chairman

This official is elected by a vote of the entire Navajo tribe to serve as chairman of the Tribal Council for a period of four years.

Tribal Council

The Tribal Council is the governing body of the Navajo tribe. Its members are elected by the Chapters and presided over by the tribal chairman.

Two-Year Man

This is a colloquialism for the commissioned officer who elects to fulfill his military service in the PHS and does not plan to remain in the Corps beyond his two-year commitment period.

Window Rock

Window Rock, Arizona, is the Navajo capital where the tribal council meets. It is also the administrative center of the reservation's federal agencies with the Area offices for both BIA and IHS.

Index